Edexcel

Foundation

GCSE Mathematics

4-Speed Revision Guide

Keith Pledger

Gareth Cole

Peter Jolly

Graham Newman

www.heinemann.co.uk
✓ Free online support
✓ Useful weblinks
✓ 24 hour online ordering

01865 888058

Harcourt is an imprint of Harcourt Education Limited, a company incorporated
in England and Wales, having its registered office: Halley Court, Jordan Hill,
Oxford OX2 8EJ.
Registered company number: 3099304

www.harcourt.co.uk

Heinemann is the registered trademark of
Harcourt Education Limited

Text © Keith Pledger, Gareth Cole, Peter Jolly and Graham Newman, 2007

First published 2007

12 11 10 09 08 07
10 9 8 7 6 5 4 3 2 1

British Library Cataloguing in Publication Data is available from the British Library on
request.

ISBN 978 0 435533 76 2

Typeset by Tech-Set Ltd, Gateshead, Tyne and Wear
Cover design by Tony Richardson
Cover photo/illustration © Digital Vision
Printed in the UK at Scotprint

Acknowledgements
Every effort has been made to contact copyright holders of material reproduced in
this book. Any omissions will be rectified in subsequent printings if notice is given to
the publishers.

Revising for your GCSE maths exam

WHY?

Because you need to be prepared for every question in the exam.

WHEN?

Sooner rather than later.

Make yourself a Revision Timetable and stick to it.

Set revision sessions of manageable length before and after school, say 10–15 minutes each to start with.

Build up to longer sessions, with short breaks every 25 minutes or so.

Don't cram the night before.

WHERE?

Choose a place where
- you will not be disturbed
- you can really concentrate
- you have all the equipment you need

1st speed – green pages – thorough revision

1 Read the key facts.

2 Follow the worked examples.

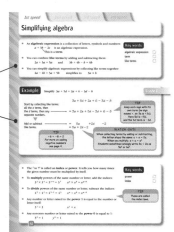

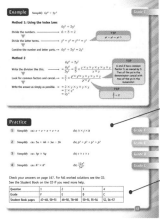

3 Do the practice questions.

4 For more help with tricky topics, read the recommended Student book pages on the CD.

2nd speed – orange pages – identify your weaknesses in detail

1 Take a topic test.

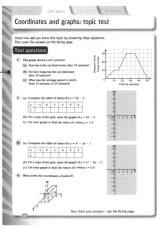

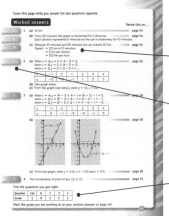

2 Check your answers against the worked solutions.

3 See the grade you are working at.

4 If you get any questions wrong, work through the recommended 1st speed pages.

3rd speed – blue pages – focus on your top priority topics

1 Take a subject test – there is one for each of Number, Algebra, Shape, space and measure and Handling data.

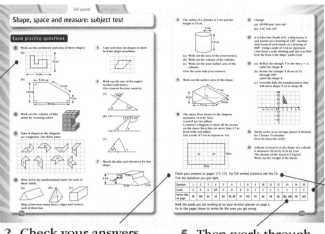

3 See the grade you are working at.

4 If you get any questions wrong check the worked solutions on the CD.

2 Check your answers.

5 Then work through the recommended 1st speed pages.

4th speed – red pages – instant overview of the key facts

1 Check that you understand the key facts for each subject.

2 Read the 1st speed pages of any topics you are not sure about.

3 Learn any formulae that are not on the formulae sheet.

Practice examination papers

1 Do the practice examination papers.

2 Use the 'Maths language in exams' page to decode what the question is asking you for.

3 For each question, how many marks is it worth? Make sure that you show all your working out to get all the marks.

4 Check your answers.

5 Check the worked solutions on the CD for any you got wrong and work through the recommended 1st speed pages.

Revision planner (pages vi–x)

The revision planner shows the contents of each page.
You can use it to help you plan your revision:

1 Tick the topics you understand.

2 After each test, mark on the grade you are working at.

Maths language in exams (page xi)

Use these pages to decode what a question really means.

Revision planner

Use this to help you plan your revision.

- Tick the topics you understand ✓
- After each test, write in the grade you are working at ⓒ

Number

Number (cont.)

Algebra

Algebra (cont.)

Shape, space and measure

Shape, space and measure (cont.)

Speed	Topic		I understand ✓
1st	**Working with angles**	page 80	
	Corresponding and alternate angles		
	Proof		
	Bearings		
2nd	**ANGLES topic test**		I am working at grade ◯
1st	**Polygons**	page 84	
	Polygons and calculating angles		
	Congruency and tessellations		
1st	**Drawing and calculating**	page 86	
	Accurate drawing, measuring and construction		
	Scale drawing and bearing		
	Locus, simple instructions		
	Pythagoras		
2nd	**2-D SHAPES topic test**		I am working at grade ◯
1st	**Units of measurement**	page 90	
	Metric units/conversion		
	Metric/imperial conversion		
	Speed		
	Timetables		
2nd	**MEASURE topic test**		I am working at grade ◯
1st	**3-D shapes**	page 94	
	Prisms		
	Nets, plans and elevations		
	Planes of symmetry		
2nd	**3-D SHAPES topic test**		I am working at grade ◯
1st	**Perimeter and area**	page 98	
	Perimeter		
	Area		
	Surface area		
	Changing/comparing units		
1st	**Volume, capacity and density**	page 100	
	Volume		
	Prisms/cylinders		
	Changing/comparing units		
	Density		
1st	**Perimeter, area and volume of shapes**	page 102	
	Circle and cylinder problems		
2nd	**PERIMETER, AREA AND VOLUME topic test**		I am working at grade ◯
1st	**Rotation, reflection and symmetry**	page 106	
	Symmetry		
	Rotation		
	Reflection		

Shape, space and measure (cont.)

Handling data

Maths language in exams

When a question says...	What it means
You must show your working...	You will lose marks if you do not show how you worked out the answer.
Estimate...	Usually means round numbers to 1 significant figure and then carry out the calculation.
Calculate...	Some working out is needed – so show it!
Work out OR Find...	A written or mental calculation is needed.
Write down...	Written working out is not usually required.
Give an exact value of...	No rounding or approximations.
Give your answer to an appropriate degree of accuracy...	If the numbers in the question are given to 2 decimal places, give your answer to 2 decimal places.
Give your answer in its simplest form...	Usually means you will need to cancel a fraction or a ratio.
Simplify...	In algebra, means collect like terms together.
Solve...	Usually means find the value of x in an equation.
Expand...	Multiply out the brackets.
Factorise...	Put in brackets with common factors outside the bracket.
Measure...	Use a ruler or a protractor to measure lengths or angles accurately.
Draw an accurate diagram...	Use a ruler and protractor to draw the diagram. Lengths must be exact and angles must be accurate.
Construct, using ruler and compasses...	Draw, using a ruler as a straight edge and compasses to draw arcs. Leave your construction lines and arcs in – don't rub them out.
Sketch...	An accurate drawing is not required; a freehand drawing will be fine.
Diagram NOT accurately drawn...	Don't measure angles or sides. If you are asked to find them, you need to work them out.
Give reasons for your answer OR Explain why...	You need to write an explanation. Show any working out, or quote any laws or theorems you used, for example Pythagoras' theorem.
Use your (the) graph...	Read values from your graph and use them.
Describe fully...	Usually means transformations: • Reflection – give the equation of the line of reflection (2 marks) • Rotation – give the angle, direction of turn and the centre of rotation (3 marks) • Enlargement – give the scale factor and the centre of enlargement (3 marks)
Give a reason for your answer...	In angle questions, means write a reason. For example: • angles in a triangle add up to $180°$ • alternate angles

Place value, ordering and rounding

- A number can be written in words or in **figures**.

- Each **digit** in a number has a value that depends on its position. This is its **place value**.

- Digits in a large number are grouped in threes, starting from the *right*, for example 456 762 121

Example

(a) Write three hundred and forty-six million, five hundred and sixty-one thousand, nine hundred and seventy-eight in figures.

(b) What is the value of the 7 in 37 385?

Grade G

Write the millions. ────────────• (a) 346 000 000   346 millions

Write the thousands. ────────────• 561 000   561 thousands

TIP
Zeros are used to show that a column is empty.

Write the hundreds, tens and units. ────────• 978   9 hundreds, 7 tens and 8 units

Combine all three parts. ──────• 346 561 978

Look at the place value column. ──────• (b) **37 385**
The 7 is in the thousands column.
It means 7 thousands or 7000.

- In whole numbers the more digits, the larger the number.

- When two numbers have the same number of digits, look at the highest place value column to see which is larger. If these digits are the same, look at the next column, and so on.

Example

Write these numbers in order of size, smallest first:

906,   894,   910,   899,   99

Grade G

Find the smallest number first. ──────• 99   99 has no hundreds so it is the smallest.

Now find the next smallest, and so on. ──────• 894   Two numbers have 8 hundreds.
894 is smaller than 899.

Now write the numbers in order. ──────• 99, 894, 899, 906, 910

WATCH OUT!
Check whether the question asks you to write them smallest first or largest first.

- To write a number to the **nearest 10,** look at the **units digit**. If it is 5 or more, **round up**. If it is less than 5, **round down**.

- To write a number to the **nearest 100**, look at the **tens digit**. If it is 5 or more, round up. If it is less than 5, round down.

- To write a number to the **nearest 1000**, look at the **hundreds digit**. If it is 5 or more, round up. If it is less than 5, round down.

Example

Write 37 385 to the nearest hundred.

Look at the tens column. ————————• 37 385

37 385 to the nearest 100 is 37 400.

TIP
8 is more than 5, so round up. The 300 becomes 400.

Grade G

Practice

1 Write 75 203 in words.

Grade G

2 Seventeen million, three hundred and fifty-four thousand people watched Coronation Street last Thursday.
Write this number in figures.

Grade G

3 Write down the value of the 8 in 56 850

Grade G

4 Write these numbers in order of size, smallest first:

88,   72,   302,   39,   267

Grade G

5 Write 56 840
(a) to the nearest thousand   (b) to the nearest hundred.

Grade G

Check your answers on page 166. For full worked solutions see the CD,
See the Student Book on the CD if you need more help.

Question	1	2	3	4	5
Grade	G	G	G	G	G
Student Book pages	1–7	1–7	1–2	2–7	20–22

Negative numbers

- **Negative numbers** represent quantities that are less than zero.

Getting larger →

$$-5 \quad -4 \quad -3 \quad -2 \quad -1 \quad 0 \quad 1 \quad 2 \quad 3 \quad 4 \quad 5$$

← Getting smaller

- Adding a negative number has the same effect as subtracting the **positive number**, for example $4 + -1 = 4 - 1 = 3$

- Subtracting a negative number has the same effect as adding the positive number, for example $2 - -3 = 2 + 3 = 5$

Example   Work out these additions and subtractions.

(a) $-2 + 3$ (b) $-2 - 3$ (c) $-2 - -3$

Grade F

To add or subtract, ⟶ (a) $-2 + 3 = 1$
use a number line.

(b) $-2 - 3 = -5$

Add the positive ⟶ (c) $-2 - -3 = -2 + 3 = 1$
number.

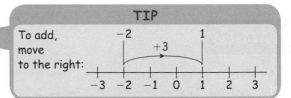

TIP

To add, move to the right:
$-2 \quad\quad 1$
$+3$
$-3 \quad -2 \quad -1 \quad 0 \quad 1 \quad 2 \quad 3$

TIP

To subtract, move to the left:
$-5 \quad\quad -2$
-3
$-6 \quad -5 \quad -4 \quad -3 \quad -2 \quad -1$

- These tables show the signs you get when you multiply or divide one number by another:

+	×	+	=	+
+	×	−	=	−
−	×	+	=	−
−	×	−	=	+

+	÷	+	=	+
+	÷	−	=	−
−	÷	+	=	−
−	÷	−	=	+

- Two **like signs** give a $+$, two **unlike signs** give a $-$

Example   Work out these multiplications and divisions.

(a) $-12 \div -3$ (b) $12 \div -3$ (c) 2×3

Grade E

First do the calculation ⟶ (a) $12 \div 3 = 4$ $-12 \div -3 = +4$

TIP
$- \div - = +$

Then use the 'like and unlike signs' rule to work out the sign for the answer.

(b) $12 \div 3 = 4$ $12 \div -3 = -4$

TIP
$+ \div - = -$

TIP
$+ \times + = +$

(c) $2 \times 3 = 6$

- As the temperature rises, the numbers get higher.
- As the temperature falls, the numbers get lower.

Example

Grade F

The temperature falls by 5° from the one shown on the thermometer. What is the new temperature?

$3 - 5 = 2$

The new temperature is $-2\,°C$.

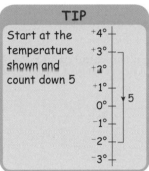

TIP
Start at the temperature shown and count down 5

$+4°$
$+3°$
$+2°$
$+1°$
$0°$ ↓5
$-1°$
$-2°$
$-3°$

Practice

Grade G
Grade F
Grade F

1 Here is a list of numbers:
$2,\ -10,\ 0,\ -6,\ -2,\ 6,\ 10$

(a) Write down the largest number.

(b) Write the numbers in order, smallest number first.

2 Work out these additions and subtractions.

(a) $5 - 6$ (b) $-5 - 6$
(c) $-5 + 6$ (d) $5 + -6$
(e) $5 - -6$ (f) $-5 - -6$

Grade F

3 Last night the temperature was $-6\,°C$.
The temperature rose by 8°.
What was the new temperature?

Grade E

4 Work out these multiplications and divisions.

(a) $+4 \times -5$ (b) $-4 \times +5$
(c) -4×-5 (d) $20 \div -5$
(e) $-20 \div +5$ (f) $-20 \div -5$
(g) $\dfrac{-24}{-6}$ (h) $\dfrac{20}{-4}$

Check your answers on page 166. For full worked solutions see the CD.
See the Student Book on the CD if you need more help.

Question	1a	1b	2	3	4
Grade	G	F	F	F	E
Student Book pages		28–29	31–32	29–30	32–34

Indices and powers

- The **power** is how many times a number is multiplied by itself, for example
  $2 \times 2 \times 2 \times 2 = 2^4$. You say '2 to the power 4'.

- A power is also called an **index** (plural **indices**).

- The **square** of 4 is $4 \times 4 = 4^2 = 16$
  $\sqrt{16} = 4$ means the **square root** of 16 is 4
  -4 is also a square root of 16 since $-4 \times -4 = 16$.
  There are two square roots, positive and negative.

- The **cube** of 4 is $4 \times 4 \times 4 = 4^3 = 64$
  $\sqrt[3]{64} = 4$ means the **cube root** of 64 is 4

- You can use a calculator to find squares, cubes, square roots and cube roots.

Key words

power ☐   square root ☐
index ☐   cube ☐
indices ☐   cube root ☐
square ☐

Example   Write down the value of   (a) 5^3 **Grade F**   (b) $\sqrt{49}$ **Grade E**

Write out the calculation in full. ⟶
(a) $5^3 = 5 \times 5 \times 5 = 25 \times 5 = 125$

(b) $\sqrt{49} = \sqrt{7 \times 7} = 7$, $\sqrt{49} = \sqrt{-7 \times -7} = -7$

- To **multiply** powers of the same number, add the indices: $3^4 \times 3^2 = 3^{4+2} = 3^6$

- To **divide** powers of the same number, subtract the indices: $4^6 \div 4^2 = 4^{6-2} = 4^4$

Example   Simplify   (a) $2^3 \times 2^4$ (b) $5^6 \div 5^4$ **Grade C**

Method 1
Write out the calculation in full. ⟶
(a) $2^3 = 2 \times 2 \times 2$
$2^4 = 2 \times 2 \times 2 \times 2$
$2^3 \times 2^4 = 2 \times 2 \times 2 \times 2 \times 2 \times 2 \times 2 = 2^7$

(b) $5^6 = 5 \times 5 \times 5 \times 5 \times 5 \times 5$
$5^4 = 5 \times 5 \times 5 \times 5$
$5^6 \div 5^4 = \dfrac{5 \times 5 \times \cancel{5} \times \cancel{5} \times \cancel{5} \times \cancel{5}}{\cancel{5} \times \cancel{5} \times \cancel{5} \times \cancel{5}} = 5^2$

Method 2
Use the rule. ⟶
(a) $2^3 \times 2^4 = 2^{3+4} = 2^7$

(b) $5^6 \div 5^4 = 5^{6-4} = 5^2$

- **BIDMAS** is a made-up word to help you remember the order of operations:

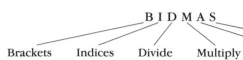

B I D M A S

Brackets   Indices   Divide   Multiply   Add   Subtract

When the operations are the same, you do them in the order they appear.

Key words

BIDMAS ☐

Example

Work out   **(a)** 3×5^2 **(b)** $5(7 - 4)$ Grade E   **(c)** $(4^2)^3$ Grade C

Work out the Index, then Multiply.   ——• (a) $3 \times 5^2 = 3 \times 25 = 75$

TIP
Remember BIDMAS!

Work out the Brackets first, then Multiply.   ——• (b) $5(7 - 4) = 5 \times 3 = 15$

TIP
$5(7 - 4)$ means 'multiply the contents of the bracket by 5'.

Work out the brackets first, then the index.   ——• (c) $(4^2)^3 = (4 \times 4)^3$
           $= 16^3 = 16 \times 16 \times 16 = 4096$

TIP
Use long multiplication twice. For more on long multiplication see pages 10–11

Practice

1   Write down the value of   **(a)** 3^3 Grade F   **(b)** $\sqrt{36}$ Grade E

2   Work out   **(a)** 4×5^3 **(b)** $3(9 - 4)$ Grade E

3   Add brackets to this calculation to make it into a true statement: Grade D
      $3 \times 4 + 5 = 3^3$

4   Simplify   **(a)** $4^3 \times 4^2$ **(b)** $9^7 \div 9^4$ **(c)** 7^0 **(d)** $(4^2)^3$ Grade C

Check your answers on page 166. For full worked solutions see the CD.
See the Student Book on the CD if you need more help.

Question	1a	1b	2	3	4
Grade	F	E	E	D	C
Student Book pages	36–39		36–39, 58–60	58–60	54–55, 58–60

Multiples, factors and primes

- The **factors** of a number are whole numbers that divide exactly into the number. The factors include 1 and the number itself.

- **Multiples** of a number are the results of multiplying the number by a positive whole number.

- A **prime number** is a whole number greater than 1 which has only two factors: itself and 1.
  1 is not a prime number as it can only be divided by one number (itself).

- A **prime factor** is a factor that is a prime number.

Key words

prime number ☐
prime factor ☐
multiple ☐
factor ☐
product of prime factors ☐

Example   Here is a list of numbers: 1, 9, 12, 6, 2, 3, 24, 5

Grade F/E

Write down the numbers that are

(a) prime numbers   **(b)** factors of 12   **(c)** multiples of 6   **(d)** prime factors of 6

Look for numbers whose only ———• (a) 2, 3 and 5
factors are 1 and the number itself.

WATCH OUT!
Write *all* the factors – don't forget the number itself (if it is in the list). Students often forget that any number is a factor of itself and they often leave out 1.

Look for numbers that divide ———• (b) 1, 2, 3, 6 and 12
exactly into 12.

Look for numbers in the 6 times table.—• (c) 6, 12 and 24

Use your list of prime numbers ———• (d) 2 and 3
from part (a).
Which ones are factors of 6?

Example   Write each of these numbers as a **product of its prime factors**.

Grade C

(a) 12   **(b)** 18

Method 1
Find the prime factors by ——•
using factor trees.

▼

(a)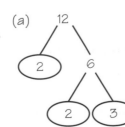

WATCH OUT!
Don't forget this step. Product means 'numbers multiplied together'.

(b)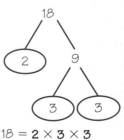

Write the number as a ———•
product of its prime factors.

$12 = 2 \times 2 \times 3$
$\quad = 2^2 \times 3$

$18 = 2 \times 3 \times 3$
$\quad = 2 \times 3^2$

Method 2

Find the prime factors by dividing by each prime number in turn.

(a) $12 \div 2 = 6$ $\quad 6 \div 2 = 3$ $\quad$ 3 is prime

$12 = 2 \times 2 \times 3 = 2^2 \times 3$

(b) $18 \div 2 = 9$ $\quad 9 \div 3 = 3$ $\quad$ 3 is prime

$18 = 2 \times 3 \times 3 = 2 \times 3^2$

- The **highest common factor** (HCF) of two numbers is the highest factor that is common to both of them.
- The **lowest common multiple** (LCM) of two numbers is the lowest multiple that is common to both of them (or the lowest number that is a multiple of them both).

Key words

lowest common multiple (LCM) ☐
highest common factor (HCF) ☐

Example

Grade C

(a) Find the highest common factor (HCF) of 12 and 18.
(b) Find the lowest common multiple (LCM) of 12 and 18.

Write each number as a product of its prime factors.
Circle the common factors and multiply them together.

(a) $12 = (2) \times 2 \times (3)$
$18 = (2) \times 3 \times (3)$
The HCF is $2 \times 3 = 6$

List the first few multiples of each number.
Circle the lowest number that appears in both lists.

(b) 12 24 (36) 48 60 72
18 (36) 54 72
The LCM is 36

Practice

1 Here is a list of numbers.
8, 16, 5, 4, 3, 18
Write down the numbers that are

Grade F (a) factors of 16

Grade F (b) multiples of 4

Grade E (c) prime numbers.

2 Write each of these numbers as a product of its prime factors. Grade C

(a) 16 (b) 24

3 Find the HCF of 16 and 24 Grade C

4 Find the LCM of 16 and 24 Grade C

Check your answers on page 166. For full worked solutions see the CD.
See the Student Book on the CD if you need more help.

Question	1ab	1c	2	3	4
Grade	F	E	C	C	C
Student Book pages	34–36		40–41	41–42	41–42

Calculating and estimating

- **Sum**, **plus**, **total** and **add** are all words that mean **addition** (+).

- **Minus**, **take away** and **difference** are all words that mean **subtraction** (−).

- **Product** and **times** are words that mean **multiplication** (×).

- **Sharing** and **goes into** are words that mean **division** (÷).

Key words

addition ☐
subtraction ☐
multiplication ☐
division ☐

Example Work out 324×56

Grade E

Traditional method

Multiply 324 by 6.

Multiply 324 by 50. Write a zero in the units column and multiply by 5.

Then add.

```
      3 2 4
      5 6 ×
    1 9 4 4
  1 6 2 0 0 +
  1 8 1 4 4
```

Grid method

300	20	4	×
15 000	1000	200	50
18 00	120	24	6

$\downarrow$ 16 800 $\downarrow$ 1120 $\downarrow$ 224 = 18 144

Example Work out $544 \div 16$

Grade E

Traditional method

16 divides into 54, **3** times remainder **6**.

16 divides into 64, **4** times.

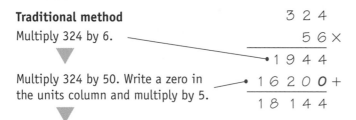

```
        3 4
  16)5 4 4
      4 8
        6 4
        6 4
```

Chunking method

Subtract 10 lots of 16 (that is 10 × 16 = 160). Repeat as many times as you can.

Subtract 16. Repeat as many times as you can.

Add up the parts of your answer.

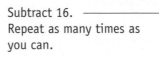

```
      5 4 4
      1 6 0 −    1 0 ⎫
      3 8 4            ⎪
      1 6 0 −    1 0 ⎬ 3
      2 2 4            ⎪
      1 6 0 −    1 0 ⎭
        6 4
        1 6 −    1 ⎫
        4 8          ⎪
        1 6 −    1 ⎪
        3 2          ⎬ 4
        1 6 −    1 ⎪
        1 6          ⎪
        1 6 −    1 ⎭
         0
```

$3 \times 10 + 4 \times 1$
$= 30 + 4 = 34$

EXAMINER'S TIP

You will find questions like this on the non-calculator paper. Make sure you get plenty of practice.

- To **estimate** the **approximate** answer to a calculation, **round** each number to **1 significant figure** (1 s.f.).

Example

(a) Estimate the answer to (i) $\dfrac{39 \times 299}{595}$ (ii) $\dfrac{975}{275 + 215}$

(b) Check your estimates from part (a) with a calculator.

Grade D

Write each number to ──────▶ (a) (i) $\dfrac{39 \times 299}{595}$ is about $\dfrac{40 \times 300}{600} = \dfrac{12000}{600} = 20$
1 significant figure.

(ii) $\dfrac{975}{275 + 215}$ is about $\dfrac{1000}{300 + 200} = \dfrac{1000}{500} = 2$

TIP

For more on rounding to 1 s.f., see page 17.

Work out the top. ──────▶ (b) (i) $\dfrac{39 \times 299}{595} = \dfrac{11\,661}{595} = 19.598\ldots$

Work out the bottom. ──────▶ (ii) $\dfrac{975}{275 + 215} = \dfrac{975}{490} = 1.989\ldots$
Then divide.

Practice

1 Work out these multiplications. Do not use a calculator.

(a) 205×34 (b) 546×53 (c) 475×28

Grade F

2 Work out these divisions. Do not use a calculator.

(a) $375 \div 15$ (b) $392 \div 16$ (c) $744 \div 24$

Grade F

3 Estimate the answer to   (a) $\dfrac{790 + 87}{295}$ (b) $\dfrac{4750}{385 - 299}$

Give your answers to 1 significant figure.

Grade D

4 Check your answers to question **3** with a calculator.

Grade D

Check your answers on page 166. For full worked solutions see the CD.
See the Student Book on the CD if you need more help.

Question	1	2	3	4
Grade	F	F	D	D
Student Book pages	13–14	15–17	23–24	23–24

Integers: topic test

Check how well you know this topic by answering these questions.
First cover the answers on the facing page.

Test questions

1 (a) Write 860 245 in words.

(b) Write 3 million, two hundred and forty thousand, five hundred and six in figures.

2 Put these numbers in order, starting with the smallest number:

67, 76, 8, 88, 79

3 Write 356 276
(a) to the nearest thousand
(b) to the nearest hundred.

4 Write down the value of the 5 in 25 360

5 Find the number that is

(a) 6 less than 8

(b) 3 less than 0

(c) 9 bigger than -5

(d) 10 greater than -15

6 Find the temperature when
(a) $3\,°C$ falls by $6°$ (b) $-4\,°C$ falls by $2°$
(c) $-1\,°C$ rises by $7°$ (d) $-13\,°C$ rises by $5°$

7 The temperature one day at noon was $-1\,°C$. The temperature fell $7°$ by midnight. What was the temperature at midnight?

8 Work out these additions and subtractions.
(a) $+9 + -17$ (b) $-3 + -1$
(c) $-12 + +3$ (d) $-6 + -6$
(e) $-4 - -5$ (f) $-11 - -4$

9 Write down the value of
(a) 5^3 (b) $\sqrt{81}$

10 Work out these multiplications and divisions.
(a) $+8 ÷ +2$ (b) $-3 × +4$
(c) $+10 ÷ -5$ (d) $-8 × -8$
(e) $-24 ÷ -6$ (f) $+6 × -9$

11 James puts bottles into boxes. Each box contains 24 bottles. One day James filled 255 boxes.

(a) How many bottles did James put into boxes?

(b) The next day James put 984 bottles into boxes. How many boxes did James fill with bottles?

12 1690 football fans booked to go by coach to see their team play away. Each coach holds 57 people. How many coaches will be needed to take all the fans?

13 Here is a list of numbers:

12, 18, 6, 7, 3, 9

Write down the numbers that are

(a) factors of 18   (b) multiples of 6

(c) prime numbers   (d) prime factors of 18

14 Work out

(a) $3 × 6^2$ (b) $6(5 + 4)$

15 (a) Work out the approximate answer for
(i) $\dfrac{399 × 52}{495}$ (ii) $\dfrac{589 + 310}{380 - 96}$
(b) Check your estimates from part (a) with a calculator.

16 Simplify
(a) $5^4 × 5^5$ (b) $3^8 ÷ 3^5$ (c) $\dfrac{4^7}{4^3}$

17 Write each of these numbers as a product of its prime factors.

(a) 18   (b) 24

18 Find

(a) the LCM and

(b) the HCF of 18 and 24

Now check your answers – see the facing page.

Cover this page while you answer the test questions opposite.

Worked answers

Revise this on...

G   1   (a) Eight hundred and sixty thousand, two hundred and forty-five   page 2
(b) 3 240 506

G   2   8, 67, 76, 79, 88   page 2

G   3   (a) 356 000   (b) 356 300   page 3

G   4   5 thousands or 5000   page 2

G/F   5   (a) $8 - 6 = 2$ (b) $0 - 3 = -3$ (c) $-5 + 9 = 4$ (d) $-15 + 10 = -5$ page 4

F   6   (a) $3 - 6 = -3\,°C$ (b) $-4 - 2 = -6\,°C$ page 5
(c) $-1 + 7 = 6\,°C$ (d) $-13 + 5 = -8\,°C$

F   7 $-1 - 7 = -8\,°C$ page 5

F   8   (a) -8 (b) -4 (c) -9 (d) -12 (e) 1 (f) 7 page 4

F   9   (a) 125   (b) 9 or -9 page 6

E   10   (a) 4   (b) -12 (c) -2 (d) 64   (e) 4   (f) -54 page 4

E   11   (a) $255 \times 24 = 6120$ bottles   (b) $984 \div 24 = 41$ boxes   page 4

E   12 $1690 \div 57 = 29$ remainder 37, so 30 coaches will be needed.   page 4

F/E/D   13   (a) 3, 6, 9 and 18   (b) 6, 12 and 18   (c) 3 and 7   (d) 3   page 8

D   14   (a) $3 \times 36 = 108$ (b) $6 \times 9 = 54$ page 7

D   15   (a) (i) $\dfrac{400 \times 50}{500} = 40$ (ii) $\dfrac{600 + 300}{400 - 100} - \dfrac{900}{300} = 3$ page 11

         (b) (i) $20\,748 \div 495 = 41.915\ldots$ (ii) $899 \div 284 = 3.165\ldots$

C   16   (a) $5^{4+5} = 5^9$ (b) $3^{8-5} = 3^3$ (c) $4^{7-3} = 4^4$ page 6

C   17   (a) $18 = 2 \times 3 \times 3$ (b) $24 = 2 \times 2 \times 2 \times 3$ page 8

C   18   (a) Multiples of 18: 18, 36, 54, 72, 90   Multiples of 24: 24, 48, 72, 96   page 9
         The LCM is 72
         (b) The HCF is $2 \times 3 = 6$

Tick the questions you got right.

Question	1	2	3	4	5a	5bcd	6	7	8	9	10	11	12	13ab	13c	13d	14	15	16	17	18
Grade	G	G	G	G	G	F	F	F	F	F	E	E	E	F	E	D	D	D	C	C	C

Mark the grade you are working at on your revision planner on page vi.

Adding, subtracting, multiplying and dividing decimals

- When working out a decimal **addition** or **subtraction**, write the numbers in columns so that the **decimal points** are underneath one another.

- The decimal point in the answer will be underneath the ones in the calculation.

Key words

add ☐
subtract ☐
decimal point ☐

Example   Work out **(a)** 2.2 + 3.09 + 15   **(b)** 3.2 − 1.86

 Grade G

Put the numbers in columns with the decimal points underneath one another. ⟶ (a)

```
    2 . 2
    3 . 0 9
  1 5 .       +
  2 0 . 2 9
        1
```

TIP
For a whole number, the decimal point goes after the units digit.

Put the numbers in columns with the decimal points underneath one another. ⟶ (b)

```
    3 . 2
    1 . 8 6 −
```

Put a zero to fill in the empty space. ⟶
Take away as usual.

```
    3 . 2 0
    1 . 8 6 −
```

```
  ²3̸ . ¹1̸²1̸0
    1 . 8 6 −
    1 . 3 4
```

EXAMINER'S TIP
Don't try to work it out in your head. Put the numbers in columns and line up the decimal points.

- When **multiplying** decimals, the answer must have the same number of **decimal places** as the total number of decimal places in the numbers being multiplied.

- Work out the multiplication without the decimal points, then put the decimal point in the answer.

Key words

multiply ☐
decimal place ☐

Example   Work out 5.26 × 3.4

 Grade C

Use the method from page 10 to work out the multiplication without decimal points. ▶

Count the total number of decimal places in the numbers you are multiplying. ▶

Put the decimal point in the answer so it has this number of decimal places.

```
      5 2 6
        3 4 ×
    2 1 0 4
  1 5 7 8 0
  1 7 8 8 4
```

5.26 × 3.4
2 d.p. + 1 d.p. = 3 d.p.

The answer must have 3 d.p. so it is 17.884

- When **dividing** decimals by decimals make sure you always divide by a whole number. You do this by multiplying both numbers in the division by 10 or 100 or 1000 etc.

Key word

divide ☐

Example

Work out **(a)** $12 \div 0.4$ **(b)** $3.2 \div 0.25$

Multiply both numbers by the same number so that you are dividing by a whole number.

(a) $12 \div 0.4$
$= 120 \div 4$
$= 30$

TIP
You need to make 0.4 into 4. Multiply *both* numbers by 10.

(b) $3.2 \div 0.25$
$= 320 \div 25$
$= 12.8$

TIP
You need to make 0.25 into 25. Multiply *both* numbers by 100.

TIP
For more on long division see page 10.

TIP
Use long division:

$$
\begin{array}{r}
12.8 \\
25\overline{)320.0} \\
\underline{25} \\
70 \\
\underline{50} \\
200 \\
\underline{200}
\end{array}
$$

Practice

1 Work out these additions. Show all your working.

(a) $1.2 + 0.45 + 14$ (b) $5.07 + 0.98 + 10$ (c) £3.46 + £5.30 + £12 + £2.09

2 Work out these subtractions. Show all your working.

(a) $4.56 - 3.8$ (b) $12.4 - 3.25$ (c) £10 − £7.24

3 Work out these multiplications. Show all your working.

(a) 5.4×7 **Grade E** (b) 24.5×2.7 **Grade D** (c) 3.46×0.62

4 Work out these divisions. Show all your working.

(a) $4.5 \div 0.5$ (b) $1.28 \div 0.4$ (c) $2.88 \div 0.24$

Check your answers on page 166. For full worked solutions see the CD.
See the Student Book on the CD if you need more help.

Question	1	2	3a	3bc	4
Grade	G	G	E	D	D
Student Book pages	89–90	90		91–92	92–94

Rounding decimals

- To **round** to a given number of **decimal places (d.p.)**, count the number of decimal places from the decimal point.

- Look at the next digit after the one you want.
  If it is 5 or more, **round up**. If it is less than 5, **round down**.

Key words

rounding ☐	decimal places ☐
round up ☐	round down ☐

Example

Write these numbers correct to 2 decimal places.

    (a) 4.679 23   **(b)** 5.234 78   **(c)** 2.895

Grade F

Count 2 digits from ⟶ the decimal point
Look at the next digit.

(a) 4.67**9** 23
   = 4.68 (to 2 d.p.)

> **TIP**
> 9 is more than 5, so round up.
> The 7 becomes 8

(b) 5.234 78
   = 5.23 (to 2 d.p.)

> **TIP**
> The next digit is 4 so round down.
> The 3 stays the same.

(c) 2.89**5**
   = 2.90 (to 2 d.p.)

> **TIP**
> The next digit is 5, so round up. 0.89 rounds up
> to 0.90. Keep the zero because you need 2 d.p.

- Write answers to money calculations to the nearest penny (2 d.p.).

Example

David bought 10 litres of fuel at three different garages.
    At Garage A it cost £18
    At Garage B it cost £2.10 more than at Garage A.
    At Garage C it cost £20.19

Work out the cost of 1 litre of fuel at each garage.

Grade F

Divide the total ⟶ cost by the
number of litres.
Write the answer to
the nearest penny
(2 d.p.).

Garage A: £18 ÷ 10 = £1.8
       1 litre costs £1.80

Garage B: Cost for 10 litres
      = £18 + £2.10 = £20.10
      £20.10 ÷ 10 = £2.01
      1 litre costs £2.01

Garage C: £20.19 ÷ 10 = £2.019
      1 litre costs £2.02 (to 2 d.p.)

> **WATCH OUT!**
> You need to add a zero so there are 2 d.p.
> £1.80 means 1 pound and 80 pence.
> £1.08 means 1 pound and 8 pence.
> The position of the zero is important!

> **EXAMINER'S TIP**
> If a question doesn't tell you how to
> give a decimal answer, give it to either
> 3 significant figures or 2 decimal
> places or the nearest penny.

- To round to a given number of **significant figures** (s.f.), count the number of digits from the first non-zero digit, starting from the *left*.

- Look at the next digit after the one you want.
  If it is 5 or more, round up. If it is less than 5, round down.

- Use zeros to show the **place value**.

Example

Write these numbers correct to 3 significant figures.

(a) 647 485   (b) 1 765 891   (c) 0.004 675 26

Count 3 non-zero digits from the left
Look at the next digit.

(a) 647 485
= 647 000 (to 3 s.f.)

TIP
The next digit is 4 so round down. The 7 stays the same. Add zeros at the end to show the size of the number.

(b) 1 765 891
= 1 770 000 (to 3 s.f.)

TIP
Keep the zeros at the front to show the place value.

(c) 0.004 675 26
= 0.004 68 (to 3 s.f.)

TIP
The next digit is 5 so round up. The 6 becomes 7. Use zeros to show the place value.

Practice

1 Rana has ten pounds fifty pence and Axel has eight pounds six pence. Write these amounts in figures.

Grade G

2 Terry buys 20 litres of petrol for £18.
Work out the cost of 1 litre of petrol.

Grade F

3 Write these numbers correct to
(a) 1 decimal place   (b) 2 decimal places.
(i) 5.4523   (ii) 10.398   (iii) 4.0562

Grade F

4 Write these numbers correct to
(a) 1 significant figure   (b) 3 significant figures.
(i) 250 398   (ii) 56 921   (iii) 0.347 23   (iv) 0.000 599 772

Grade E

Check your answers on page 166. For full worked solutions see the CD.
See the Student Book on the CD if you need more help.

Question	1	2	3	4
Grade	G	F	F	E
Student Book pages	81–82	84–87	87–89	81–82

Decimals and rounding: topic test

Check how well you know this topic by answering these questions.
First cover the answers on the facing page.

Test questions

1 Work out these calculations. Show all your working.
  (a) 23.5 + 12.54 + 0.66
  (b) 5.44 + 15 + 19.85
  (c) 4.87 − 1.53
  (d) 3.00 − 1.37

2 Henri saves what is left of his pocket money each week.
In the last month he saved the following amounts each week.
     £2.55,   £3.27,   £1.95,   £3.27
How much did Henri save altogether last month?

3 Rosie bought a clock for £17.65. She paid with a £20 note.
How much change should she get?

4 Katrin has one pound fourteen pence, Joe has one pound four pence, and Susan has one pound forty pence.
Write these amounts in figures.

5 Write these numbers correct to 2 decimal places.
  (a) 5.775   (b) 0.7757
  (c) 3.999   (d) 0.779
  (e) 23.0055   (f) 25.794

6 Shaun buys 6 pints of milk. The bill comes to £1.86
Work out the cost of 1 pint.

7 Maria sells 45 packets of coloured gel pens for £5.49 each.
How much money does she collect altogether?

8 Josie bought 16 identical teddy bears for £68.
  (a) How much did she pay for each one?
  (b) She sold all the bears for £5.95 each. What is her total profit?

9 Keri buys 5 kg of potatoes. The total cost is £2.00
Work out the cost of 1 kg.

10 Tom buys a pack of 10 pens. The pack of pens cost £3.75
Find the cost of 1 pen.

11 Write these numbers correct to 3 significant figures.
  (a) 34 565   (b) 6885
  (c) 34.87   (d) 5.5683
  (e) 0.023 57   (f) 0.004 899

Now check your answers – see the facing page.

Cover this page while you answer the test questions opposite.

Worked answers

Revise this on...

G **1**
(a)
```
  23.5
  12.54
   0.66+
  36.70
   1  1
```
(b)
```
   5.44
  15
  19.85+
  40.29
   2 1
```
(c)
```
  4.87
  1.53-
  3.34
```
(d)
```
  2³.⁹0̸¹0
  1. 37-
  1. 63
```
page 14

G **2**
```
  £2.55
  £3.27
  £1.95
  £3.27+
 £11.04
   2  2
```
3
```
 £¹2⁹0̸.⁹0̸¹0
 £17.65-
 £  2.35
```
page 14

G **4**   Katrin £1.14, Joe £1.04, Susan £1.40   page 16

E **5**
(a) 5.78   (b) 0.78   (c) 4.00
(d) 0.78   (e) 23.01   (f) 25.79
page 16

E **6**   £0.31 or 31p   page 15

D **7**
```
    549
     45×
   2745
  21960
  24705
   1  1
```
£5.48 × 45 = £247.05

8 (a)
```
        4.25
  16 )68.00
      64
      40
      32
       80    £4.25 each
```
(b) £5.95 × 16 = £95.20
£95.20 − £68 = £27.20
page 15

D **9**   £0.40 or 40p   page 15

D **10**   £0.38 or 38p   page 15

C **11**
(a) 34 600   (b) 6890   (c) 34.9
(d) 5.57   (e) 0.0236   (f) 0.004 90
page 17

Tick the questions you got right.

Question	1	2	3	4	5	6	7	8	9	10	11
Grade	G	G	G	G	E	E	D	D	D	D	C

Mark the grade you are working at on your revision planner on page vi.

Understanding and simplifying fractions

- In a **fraction**, the bottom number tells you how many parts the whole has been divided into.

- Top heavy fractions, e.g. $\frac{11}{9}$, are also called **improper fractions**.

- An improper fraction can also be written as a **mixed number** (a mixture of a whole number and a fraction), and a mixed number can also be written as an improper fraction.

  improper fraction —— $\frac{11}{9} = \frac{9}{9} + \frac{2}{9} = 1\frac{2}{9}$ —— mixed number

Key words

fraction	☐
improper fraction	☐
mixed number	☐

Example   Write $\frac{15}{4}$ as a mixed number.

Grade G

Draw diagrams divided into ——— quarters.
Shade 15 quarters.
Count the wholes and count ——— the quarters.

$3\frac{3}{4}$

- Fractions can be **simplified** if the numerator (top) and denominator (bottom) have a common factor.

$$\frac{8}{12} \ \overset{\div 4}{\underset{\div 4}{\text{simplifies to}}} \ \frac{2}{3} \qquad \text{The common factor is } 4$$

This is also called **cancelling.**

- A fraction in its **lowest terms** cannot be simplified any more. The top and bottom of the fraction have no common factor.

- **Equivalent fractions** are fractions that have the same value.

$$\frac{8}{12} = \frac{4}{6} = \frac{2}{3}$$

Key words

simplify	☐
cancelling	☐
lowest terms	☐
equivalent fractions	☐

TIP
To find equivalent fractions, multiply the top and bottom of the fraction by the same number.

Example   Write $\frac{12}{18}$ as a fraction in its lowest terms.

Grade F

Find the common factors of ——— the top and bottom numbers.
Divide top and bottom by each common factor.

$\frac{12}{18} = \frac{6}{9}$ Divide top and bottom by 2

$= \frac{2}{3}$ Divide top and bottom by 3

WATCH OUT!
You need to find *all* the common factors.

Example

Write two fractions that are equivalent to $\frac{3}{4}$

Grade F

Multiply top and bottom of the fraction by the same number. ——→ $\frac{3}{4} = \frac{6}{8}$ Multiply top and bottom by 2

$\frac{3}{4} = \frac{9}{12}$ Multiply top and bottom by 3

- To compare the sizes of fractions, represent them as parts of a rectangle.

Example

Which fraction is larger, $\frac{2}{3}$ or $\frac{3}{4}$?

Grade F

Split the rectangle into thirds and into quarters. Shade 2 thirds and 3 quarters.

TIP
The lowest common multiple of 3 and 4 is 12 so your rectangle should be split into 12 squares.

$\frac{2}{3} = 8$ parts $\frac{3}{4} = 9$ parts $\frac{3}{4}$ is larger.

TIP
Split a rectangle in two directions so you can compare the fractions.

Example

Work out $\frac{3}{5}$ of £40.

Grade F

First work out 1 fifth ($\frac{1}{5}$). ——→ £40 ÷ 5 = £8

Multiply by 3 to find $\frac{3}{5}$. ——→ £8 × 3 = £24

EXAMINER'S TIP
Always show your working. You may get marks for the correct method, even if you make a mistake in the calculation.

Practice

Grade G

1 Shade $\frac{4}{5}$ of this shape.

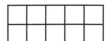

Grade G

2 Write
(a) $\frac{12}{5}$ as a mixed number
(b) $3\frac{2}{3}$ as an improper fraction.

3 Write $\frac{18}{24}$ as a fraction in its lowest terms.

Grade F

4 Write two fractions that are equivalent to $\frac{5}{6}$.

Grade F

5 Which fraction is larger, $\frac{4}{5}$ or $\frac{3}{4}$?

Grade F

6 Work out $\frac{3}{4}$ of £20

Grade F

Check your answers on page 166. For full worked solutions see the CD.
See the Student Book on the CD if you need more help.

Question	1	2	3	4	5	6
Grade	G	G	F	F	F	F
Student Book pages	151–152	153–154	156–158	158–159	160–161	155

Working with fractions

- To **add** or **subtract** fractions, find equivalent fractions that have the same **denominator** (bottom number).

$$\overset{\times 3}{\frac{1}{2}} + \frac{4}{6} = \overset{\times 3}{\frac{3}{6}} + \frac{4}{6} = \frac{7}{6} \qquad \frac{4}{6} - \overset{\times 3}{\frac{1}{2}} = \frac{4}{6} - \frac{3}{6} = \frac{1}{6}$$

Key words

equivalent fractions ☐
denominator ☐
numerator ☐
mixed number ☐

- To add or subtract mixed numbers, deal with the whole number parts first.

Example

Work out (a) $\frac{2}{3} + \frac{3}{5}$ **Grade E** (b) $5\frac{3}{4} - 2\frac{2}{3}$ **Grade C**

Write two lists of equivalent fractions.

$$\text{(a)} \quad \frac{2}{3} = \frac{4}{6} = \frac{6}{9} = \frac{8}{12} = \boxed{\frac{10}{15}} = \frac{12}{18}$$

Look for fractions with the same denominator.

$$\frac{3}{5} = \frac{6}{10} = \boxed{\frac{9}{15}} = \frac{12}{20}$$

$$\frac{2}{3} + \frac{3}{5} = \frac{10}{15} + \frac{9}{15} = \frac{19}{15}$$

Add the numerators.

$$= 1\frac{4}{15}$$

Write as a mixed number.

First subtract the whole numbers.

$$\text{(b)} \quad 5 - 2 = 3$$

Then subtract the fractions.

$$\frac{3}{4} - \frac{2}{3} = \frac{9}{12} - \frac{8}{12} = \frac{1}{12}$$

$$3 \text{ and } \frac{1}{12} \text{ is } 3\frac{1}{12}$$

Now put the whole numbers and fractions back together.

$$\text{So } 5\frac{3}{4} - 2\frac{2}{3} = 3\frac{1}{12}$$

TIP

$$\frac{3}{4} = \frac{6}{8} = \boxed{\frac{9}{12}} = \frac{12}{16}$$
$$\frac{2}{3} = \frac{4}{6} = \frac{6}{9} = \boxed{\frac{8}{12}} = \frac{10}{15}$$

- To **multiply** two fractions, multiply the numerators together and multiply the denominators together.

$$\frac{3}{4} \times \frac{4}{7} = \frac{12}{28}$$

- To **divide** fractions, invert the dividing fraction (turn it upside down) and multiply.

Turn ÷ into ×

$$\frac{1}{4} \div \frac{2}{5} = \frac{1}{4} \times \frac{5}{2} = \frac{5}{8}$$

Invert (turn upside down)

Key words

improper fraction ☐
mixed number ☐

- To multiply or divide **mixed numbers**, first change them to **improper fractions**.

$$1\frac{1}{2} \times 2\frac{1}{3} = \frac{3}{2} \times \frac{7}{3}$$

Example

Work out (a) $2\frac{1}{4} \times 1\frac{1}{5}$ (b) $5\frac{1}{2} \div 1\frac{5}{6}$

Write as improper fractions. ⎯⎯⎯⎯⎯⎯⎯ (a) $2\frac{1}{4} = \frac{9}{4}$ and $1\frac{1}{5} = \frac{6}{5}$

Multiply the top numbers and the bottom numbers. ⎯⎯⎯ $\frac{9}{4} \times \frac{6}{5} = \frac{54}{20}$

Change to a mixed number then simplify the ⎯⎯⎯⎯⎯ $= 2\frac{14}{20} = 2\frac{7}{10}$
fraction part.

Write as improper fractions. ⎯⎯⎯⎯⎯⎯⎯ (b) $5\frac{1}{2} = \frac{11}{2}$ and $1\frac{5}{6} = \frac{11}{6}$

> **TIP**
>
> 11 and 2 are common factors. You could cancel *before* multiplying.
>
> $\frac{^{1}11}{2} \times \frac{6}{11^{1}}$
>
> $= \frac{^{3}6}{2^{1}} = 3$

Invert the dividing fraction and change ÷ to ×. ⎯⎯ $\frac{11}{2} \div \frac{11}{6} = \frac{11}{2} \times \frac{6}{11}$

Multiply the top numbers and the bottom numbers. ⎯⎯⎯ $= \frac{66}{??} = 3$
Simplify the fraction.

Practice

1 Work out

(a) $\frac{1}{3} + \frac{3}{4}$

(b) $2\frac{3}{8} + 5\frac{5}{6}$

2 Work out

(a) $\frac{7}{8} - \frac{1}{3}$

(b) $5\frac{2}{3} - 2\frac{1}{4}$

3 Work out

(a) $\frac{3}{4} \times \frac{7}{12}$ (b) $3\frac{3}{4} \times 1\frac{1}{3}$

4 Work out

(a) $\frac{5}{12} \div \frac{3}{10}$ (b) $3\frac{1}{2} \div 5\frac{1}{4}$

5

A ⎯⎯⎯⎯ $2\frac{3}{4}$ miles ⎯⎯ B ⎯⎯⎯⎯⎯ C

The diagram shows three towns, A, B and C.
The distance from town A to town C is $4\frac{1}{3}$ miles.
How far is it from town B to town C?

Check your answers on page 166. For full worked solutions see the CD.
See the Student Book on the CD if you need more help.

Question	1a	1b	2a	2b	3	4	5
Grade	E	C	D	C	C	C	C
Student Book pages	161–164		165–167		167–170	170–171	171–173

Fractions: topic test

Check how well you know this topic by answering these questions.
First cover the answers on the facing page.

Test questions

1 Shade $\frac{5}{6}$ of this diagram.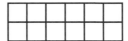

2 Write $\frac{11}{4}$ as a mixed number.

3 Express these fractions in their lowest terms.

(a) $\frac{24}{26}$ (b) $\frac{15}{20}$

4 Copy and complete these sets of equivalent fractions.

(a) $\frac{5}{8} = \frac{}{16} = \frac{}{24} = \frac{}{32} = \frac{}{40} = \frac{}{48} = \frac{}{64}$

(b) $\frac{2}{7} = \frac{}{14} = \frac{}{21} = \frac{}{28} = \frac{}{35} = \frac{}{63} = \frac{}{84}$

5 Find the difference between $\frac{3}{4}$ of 32 and $\frac{2}{3}$ of 27.

6 Henlow to Hitchin is $6\frac{1}{2}$ miles.
Clifton to Hitchin is $7\frac{1}{3}$ miles.
How much further is it to Hitchin from Clifton than from Henlow?

7 A television was reduced from £320 to £280 in a sale.
By what fraction was the price reduced in the sale?

8 There are 56 kg of potatoes in a sack.
How many $2\frac{1}{2}$ kg bags can be filled from one sack?

9 Work out

(a) $\frac{4}{9} + \frac{2}{9}$ (b) $\frac{7}{12} + \frac{1}{3}$ (c) $2\frac{1}{2} + 3\frac{1}{4}$

(d) $\frac{7}{10} - \frac{3}{10}$ (e) $\frac{5}{6} - \frac{2}{5}$ (f) $4\frac{2}{3} - 2\frac{5}{8}$

(g) $\frac{1}{3} \times \frac{1}{4}$ (h) $\frac{4}{5} \times \frac{3}{8}$ (i) $2\frac{1}{2} \times 3\frac{1}{4}$

(j) $\frac{5}{9} \div \frac{3}{5}$ (k) $1\frac{1}{4} \div 3\frac{1}{2}$ (l) $15 \div \frac{3}{5}$

Now check your answers – see the facing page.

Cover this page while you answer the test questions opposite.

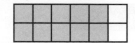

Worked answers

Revise this on...

G   1

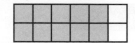

page 20

G   2 $\frac{11}{4} = 2\frac{3}{4}$

page 20

F   3   (a) $\frac{24}{36} = \frac{12}{18} = \frac{6}{9} = \frac{2}{3}$ (b) $\frac{15}{20} = \frac{3}{4}$

page 20

F   4   (a) $\frac{5}{8} = \frac{10}{16} = \frac{15}{24} = \frac{20}{32} = \frac{25}{40} = \frac{30}{48} = \frac{40}{64}$

pages 20–21

         (b) $\frac{2}{7} = \frac{4}{14} = \frac{6}{21} = \frac{8}{28} = \frac{10}{35} = \frac{18}{63} = \frac{24}{84}$

E   5 $\frac{3}{4}$ of 32 = 24 and $\frac{2}{3}$ of 27 = 18

page 21

      24 − 18 = 6

D   6 $7\frac{1}{3} - 6\frac{1}{2} = 7\frac{2}{6} - 6\frac{3}{6} = \frac{5}{6}$

page 22

      It is $\frac{5}{6}$ mile further.

D   7   Reduction = £320 − £280 = £40

page 21

      Fraction = $\frac{£40}{£320} = \frac{1}{8}$

C   8 $56 \div 2\frac{1}{2} = \frac{56}{1} \div \frac{5}{2} = \frac{56}{1} \times \frac{2}{5} = \frac{112}{5} = 22\frac{2}{5}$

pages 22–23

      22 full sacks of potatoes, with 1 kg left over

   9   (a) $\frac{4}{9} + \frac{2}{9} = \frac{6}{9}$ (b) $\frac{7}{12} + \frac{4}{12} = \frac{11}{12}$

pages 22–23

E

         (c) $5\frac{2+1}{4} = 5\frac{3}{4}$ (d) $\frac{7}{10} - \frac{3}{10} = \frac{4}{10} = \frac{2}{5}$

         (e) $\frac{25 - 12}{30} = \frac{13}{30}$ (f) $2\frac{16 - 15}{24} = 2\frac{1}{24}$

D

         (g) $\frac{1 \times 1}{3 \times 4} = \frac{1}{12}$ (h) $\frac{4 \times 3}{5 \times 8} = \frac{12}{40} = \frac{3}{10}$

         (i) $\frac{5}{2} \times \frac{13}{4} = \frac{65}{8} = 8\frac{1}{8}$ (j) $\frac{5}{9} \times \frac{5}{3} = \frac{25}{27}$

C

         (k) $\frac{5}{4} \div \frac{7}{2} = \frac{5}{4} \times \frac{2}{7} = \frac{10}{28} = \frac{5}{14}$ (l) $\frac{15}{1} \div \frac{3}{5} = \frac{15}{1} \times \frac{5}{3} = \frac{75}{3} = 25$

Tick the questions you got right.

Question	1	2	3	4	5	6	7	8	9a–d	9e–h	9i–l
Grade	G	G	F	F	E	D	D	C	E	D	C

Mark the grade you are working at on your revision planner on page vii.

Percentages, fractions and decimals

- To compare **fractions**, **decimals** and **percentages** you can change them all to percentages.

- To write a decimal as a percentage you multiply by 100.

- To write a fraction as a percentage you change it to a decimal first by dividing the **denominator** into the **numerator**.

Key words

percentage ☐   numerator ☐
decimal ☐   denominator ☐
fraction ☐

Example

Write these numbers in order of size, smallest first:

0.77,   72%, $\frac{3}{4}$, $\frac{4}{5}$,   79%

Grade E

Change all the numbers to percentages.

$0.77 \times 100 = 77$ so $0.77 = $ **77%**

72% is already a percentage.

$\frac{3}{4} = 3 \div 4 = 0.75 = $ **75%**

$\frac{4}{5} = 4 \div 5 = 0.8 = $ **80%**

79% is already a percentage.

TIP
Divide the bottom number into the top number to change a fraction to a decimal.

TIP
Multiply by 100 to change a decimal to a percentage.

EXAMINER'S TIP
Always show your working so that you can gain marks for the correct method.

Write the percentages in order.

72%, 75%, 77%, 79%, 80%

Write the original numbers in the correct order.

72%, $\frac{3}{4}$, 0.77, 79%, $\frac{4}{5}$

WATCH OUT!
Don't forget this final step.

- To compare different **proportions** you can change them all to percentages, so you are comparing like with like.

Key word

proportion ☐

Example

Jack scored 50 out of 75 in science, 56 out of 80 in maths and 45 out of 60 in English.
In which subject did he do best?

Grade D

Change all the marks into fractions and then into decimals by dividing.
Change the decimals into percentages by multiplying by 100.
Compare the percentages.

Science: $\frac{50}{75} = 50 \div 75 = 0.66\ldots = $ **66.7%**

Maths: $\frac{56}{80} = 56 \div 80 = 0.7 = $ **70%**

English: $\frac{45}{60} = 45 \div 60 = 0.75 = $ **75%**

He did best in English.

- To find a percentage of an amount you can:
  - change the percentage to a fraction and multiply *or*
  - change the percentage to a decimal and multiply *or*
  - work from 10%

Example — Work out 15% of £60

Grade E

Method 1
Write the percentage as a fraction ──▶ $\frac{15}{100} \times £60 = \frac{15 \times £60}{100} = \frac{£900}{100} = £9$
with denominator 100 and multiply.

TIP
For more on multiplying decimals see pages 14–15.

Method 2
Write the percentage as a decimal ──▶ $0.15 \times £60 = £9$
and multiply.

Method 3
Divide by 10 to find 10% ──────────▶ 10% of £60 = £60 ÷ 10 = £6

TIP
5% is half of 10%

Find 5% by dividing 10% by 2 ──────▶ 5% of £60 = £6 ÷ 2 = £3

Add 10% and 5% ───────────────────▶ £6 + £3 = £9

Practice

1 Write these numbers in order of size, smallest first:

   67%, $\frac{2}{3}$, $\frac{3}{5}$, 0.65, 63%

Grade E

2 Work out 15% of **(a)** 40 kg **(b)** £120

Grade E

3 Work out 40% of £80

Grade E

4 Work out $7\frac{1}{2}$% of £200

Grade E

5 Bobbi scored 45 out of 60 in French, 60 out of 90 in German
   and 60 out of 80 in Spanish.
   In which language did she do best?

Grade D

Check your answers on page 166. For full worked solutions see the CD.
See the Student Book on the CD if you need more help.

Question	1	2	3	4	5
Grade	E	E	E	E	D
Student Book pages	292–293	282–283	282–283	282–283	292–293

Using percentages

- To **increase** a number by a percentage, you find the percentage of that number and then add this to the starting number.

- To **decrease** a number by a percentage, you find the percentage of that number and then subtract this from the starting number.

- **Sale prices** and **discounts** involve percentage decreases.

- **VAT** and **interest** involve percentage increases.

Key words

percentage increase and decrease ☐
discount ☐
sale price ☐
VAT ☐
interest rate ☐
percentage change ☐

Example

(a) A shop gives 20% discount on electrical goods. Work out the price of a TV that normally costs £80.

(b) Jay has to pay a bill of £80 plus VAT. What is the total bill?

Grade D

TIP
You could use Method 1 or Method 2 from page 27 instead.

Find 20% of the original price. → (a) 10% of £80 = £8
So 20% of £80 = £16

Subtract this from the original price. → New price = £80 − £16 = £64

Find 17½% of the original bill. → (b) 10% of £80 = £8
5% of £80 = £4
$2\frac{1}{2}$% of £80 = £2
$17\frac{1}{2}$% of £80 = £14

Add this to the original amount. → Total bill = £80 + £14
= £94

TIP
To find $17\frac{1}{2}$% of an amount:
find 10%
find 5%   ($\frac{1}{2}$ of 10%)
find $2\frac{1}{2}$%   ($\frac{1}{2}$ of 5%)
Total = $17\frac{1}{2}$%

EXAMINER'S TIP
Make sure you understand percentages. There are always percentage calculations on GCSE papers.

- To write one number as a percentage of another:
  - write the amounts as a fraction
  - convert the fraction to a decimal
  - change the decimal to a percentage by multiplying by 100

Example

Alice buys a watch for £40 and sells it for £50. What is her percentage profit?

Grade D

Work out the profit. → Profit = £50 − £40 = £10

Write the profit as a fraction of the original price. → $\frac{£10}{£40} = \frac{1}{4}$

Change the fraction to a decimal and then a percentage. → $\frac{1}{4} = 0.25 = 25\%$

WATCH OUT!
Remember to put the *original* amount on the bottom. Students often use the final amount by mistake.

- An **index number** shows how a quantity changes over time.

- A **price index** shows how the price of something changes over time.
  - The index always starts at 100.
  - An index greater than 100 shows a price rise.
  - An index less than 100 shows a price fall.

Example

Grade C

The table shows the index numbers for the prices of houses in London over a 50-year period.

1960	1970	1980	1990	2000	2010
100	220	300	250	300	350

(a) A house cost £50 000 in 1960. How much would it have cost in 2000?

(b) What can you say about house prices between 1960 and 2000?

Divide the 1960 price by 100 to find 1%.
Then multiply by the index number for the year 2000.

(a) $\dfrac{£50\ 000}{100} \times 300 = £150\ 000$

(b) Prices went up until 1980, fell between 1980 and 1990, and then rose again after 1990.

Practice

Grade D

1 A shop reduces all its prices by 15%. Find the new cost of
  (a) a TV that normally costs £90
  (b) a DAB radio that normally costs £75

Grade D

2 Tom has to pay a garage bill of £160. VAT is added to the bill at $17\frac{1}{2}\%$.
What is the total garage bill?

3 Jade invests £400 at 5% simple interest.
  (a) How much interest will Jade receive after 1 year?
  (b) How much interest will Jade receive after 3 years?

Grade D

4 A coat is reduced in price from £60 to £48.
What is the percentage reduction?

Grade D

Check your answers on page 166. For full worked solutions see the CD.
See the Student Book on the CD if you need more help.

Question	1	2	3	4
Grade	D	D	D	D
Student Book pages	285–286	286–287	283–285	290–292

Percentages: topic test

Check how well you know this topic by answering these questions.
First cover the answers on the facing page.

Test questions

1 Work out 10% of

   (a) £50

   (b) 80 metres

   (c) 300 km

2 Complete this table of equivalent fractions, decimals and percentages.

Fraction	Decimal	Percentage
	0.5	
		30%
$\frac{1}{4}$		
	0.65	
		75%

3 Rearrange these numbers in order of size, starting with the smallest:

   $\frac{37}{100}$,   34%, $\frac{7}{20}$,   0.36

4 Sharon bought a new car for £10 000.
It lost 30% of its value in 3 years.

   (a) Work out the loss in value.

   (b) What is the value of the car after 3 years?

5 Find the percentage reduction of the sunglasses.

SUNGLASSES

Sale Price **£8**

Normal Price £10

6 Jerry invested £200 at 8% simple interest for 2 years.
How much interest did she receive?

7 Narinda earns £250 a week.
She gets a pay rise of 4%.
How much will she now earn?

8 Work out the cost of a hot tub that costs £4000 plus VAT at 17.5%.

9 A trombone costs £450 plus VAT at $17\frac{1}{2}$%.
Work out the total cost of the trombone.

10 The table shows the index numbers for the average price of new small cars.

1960	1970	1980	1990	2000	2005
100	190	280	650	850	800

   (a) In which period was there the biggest increase in prices?

   (b) A new car cost £700 in 1960.
What would a similar car have cost in 2000?

Now check your answers – see the facing page.

Cover this page while you answer the test questions opposite.

Worked answers

Revise this on...

F 1 (a) £50 ÷ 10 = £5   (b) 80 m ÷ 10 = 8 m   page 27
(c) 300 km ÷ 10 = 30 km

E 2   page 26

Fraction	Decimal	Percentage
$\frac{1}{2}$	0.5	50%
$\frac{3}{10}$	0.3	30%
$\frac{1}{4}$	0.25	25%
$\frac{13}{20}$	0.65	65%
$\frac{3}{4}$	0.75	75%

E 3 Change into percentages: page 26
$\frac{37}{100} = 37\%$, 34%, $\frac{7}{20} = 0.35 = 35\%$, $0.36 = 36\%$
The order is 34%, $\frac{7}{20}$, 0.36, $\frac{37}{100}$

D 4 (a) Loss in value = 30% of £10 000   10% = £1000 so 30% = £3000   page 28
(b) £10 000 − £3000 = £7000

D 5 Reduction = £10 − £8 = £2   Percentage reduction = $\frac{£2}{£10} \times 100 = 20\%$ page 28

D 6 Interest for 1 year = 8% of £200   10% of £200 = £20   page 28
                                       2% of £200 = £20 ÷ 5 = £4
                                       8% = £20 − £4 = £16
Interest for 2 years = 2 × £16 = £32

D 7 Increase in pay = 4% of £250 = $\frac{4}{100} \times £250 = \frac{£1000}{100} = £10$ page 28
Narindar will now earn £250 + £10 = £260

D 8 VAT = $17\frac{1}{2}\%$ of £4000   10% of £4000 = £400   page 28
                                5% of £4000 = £200
                              $2\frac{1}{2}\%$ of £4000 = £100
               So $17\frac{1}{2}\%$ of £4000 = £700
Total cost = £4000 + £700 = £4700

D 9 VAT = 17½% of £450   10% of £450 = £45   page 28
                          5% of £450 = £22.50
                         $2\frac{1}{2}\%$ of £450 = £11.25
                  So $17\frac{1}{2}\%$ of £450 = £78.75
Total cost = £450 + £78.75 = £528.75

C 10 (a) 1980–1990   (b) $\frac{£700}{100} \times 850 = £5950$ page 29

Tick the questions you got right.

Question	1	2	3	4	5	6	7	8	9	10
Grade	F	E	E	D	D	D	D	D	D	C

Mark the grade you are working at on your revision planner on page vii.

Ratio

- A **ratio** is a way of comparing two numbers or quantities.

- To **simplify** a ratio you divide both its numbers by a **common factor**.

- When a ratio cannot be simplified it is in its **lowest terms**.

- Two ratios are **equivalent** when they both simplify to the same ratio.

Key words

ratio ☐
simplify ☐
common factor ☐
lowest terms ☐
equivalent ratios ☐

Example   Simplify these ratios.   **(a)** $18:12$ **(b)** $15:10$

Grade E

Find a common factor — a number that divides into both numbers.

▼

Repeat until there are no more common factors.

(a) $18:12$ Divide both numbers by 2
    $= 9:6$ Divide both numbers by 3
    $= 3:2$

(b) $15:10$
    $= 3:2$

TIP

Equivalent ratios are like equivalent fractions. $18:12$ and $15:10$ are equivalent ratios because they both simplify to $3:2$

- Ratios written in the form $1:n$ or $n:1$ are in **unitary form**.
  For example, the ratio $3:2$ can be written as $1:\frac{2}{3}$ or $1.5:1$

Key words

unitary form ☐

Example   **(a)** Write the ratio $2:5$ in the form $1:n$

          (b) Write the ratio $2:5$ in the form $n:1$

Grade E

Divide both numbers in the ratio by the number that makes the correct number into 1.

(a) $\mathbf{2:5}$ Divide both numbers by **2**
   $= 1:2.5$

(b) $\mathbf{2:5}$ Divide both numbers by **5**
   $= 0.4:1$

TIP

Divide by 2 to give the ratio in the form $1:n$

TIP

Divide by 5 to give the ratio in the form $n:1$

- To share an amount in a given ratio:
  - find the total of all the numbers in the ratio
  - split the amount into fractions with that total as denominator.

Example

Deepal and Colette share £35 in the ratio $3:2$

(a) What fraction of the amount does each receive? **Grade E**

(b) How much money does each receive? **Grade C**

Add the two numbers in the ratio to give a total.
Write each share as a fraction with this total as denominator.

→ (a) $3 + 2 = 5$

Deepal receives $\frac{3}{5}$

Colette receives $\frac{2}{5}$

TIP
This means that the £35 is divided into **fifths**.

Divide the amount to be shared by this total.
This is one part.
Multiply this by the number of parts each person receives.

→ (b) One-fifth of £35 = £35 ÷ **5** = £7

Deepal receives $\frac{3}{5}$ = **3** × £7 = £21

Colette receives $\frac{2}{5}$ = **2** × £7 = £14

Practice

1 Write these ratios in their lowest terms. **Grade D**

(a) $6:4$ (b) $10:5$ (c) $12:8$ (d) $20:15$

2 Which of the ratios in question **1** are equivalent ratios? **Grade E**

3 (a) Write these ratios in the form $n:1$ (i) $5:4$ (ii) $2:3$ **Grade E**
   (b) Write these ratios in the form $1:n$ (i) $5:4$ (ii) $2:3$

4 Wayne and Tracey share £24 in the ratio $5:3$

(a) What fraction of £24 does Wayne receive? **Grade E**

(b) How much money does each receive? **Grade C**

Check your answers on page 166. For full worked solutions see the CD.
See the Student Book on the CD if you need more help.

Question	1	2	3	4a	4b
Grade	D	E	E	E	C
Student Book pages	324–326	326–327	327–328	328–330	

Proportion

- Two quantities are in **direct proportion** if their **ratio** stays the same when the quantities increase or decrease.

- In the **unitary method**, you find the value of *one* item first.

Key words

ratio ☐
proportion ☐
unitary method ☐

Example   Seven pens cost 84p.
How much do ten identical pens cost?

Grade D

Write down what you know. ⟶ 7 pens cost 84p

Find the cost of one by dividing. ⟶ 1 pen costs 84p ÷ 12 = 7p

Find the cost of what you need ⟶ 10 pens cost 10 × 7p = 70p
by multiplying.

TIP
In the *unitary* method you always think about *one* item first.

EXAMINER'S TIP
This type of question often comes up on GCSE papers.

Example   Here is a list of ingredients for making 12 cakes:

Grade D

200 g sugar
200 g butter
800 g flour
2 eggs
100 g dried fruit

(a) How many eggs would you need to make 18 cakes?

(b) How many grams of sugar would you need to make 9 cakes?

Look at the ratio of the numbers of cakes. ⟶ (a) 12 : 18

× $1\frac{1}{2}$
12 cakes take 2 eggs
18 cakes take 2 × $1\frac{1}{2}$ = 3 eggs

Use the unitary method. ⟶ (b) 12 cakes take 200 grams
1 cake takes $\frac{200}{12}$ grams
9 cakes take 9 × $\frac{200}{12}$ = 3 × $\frac{200}{4}$
= 3 × 50
= 150 grams

EXAMINER'S TIP
Changing a recipe for a different number of people is often tested in GCSE papers.

- Ratios called **scales** are used to show the relationship between distances on a map and distances on the ground.

Example

Two towns are 8.5 cm apart on a map.
The scale of the map is 1 : 50 000
How far apart are the towns in real life?

Write down the scale of the map. ⟶ 1 cm represents 50 000 cm

Multiply by the map ⟶ 8.5 cm represents 8.5 × 50 000 cm
distance.   = 425 000 cm

TIP
Divide by 100 to change cm to metres.

Change to suitable units. ⟶ 425 000 cm = 4250 m
4250 m = 4.25 km

TIP
For more on changing units, see pages 90–91.

TIP
Divide by 1000 to change metres to km.

Practice

1   Three packets of sweets cost £2.40
    Work out the cost of five packets of sweets.

2   Here is a list of ingredients for making 10 cakes:

    200 g sugar
    200 g butter
    800 g flour
    2 eggs

    (a) How many eggs would you need to make 25 cakes?

    (b) How many grams of sugar would you need to make 15 cakes?

3   Two villages are 4 cm apart on a map.
    The scale of the map is 1 : 25 000
    How far apart are the two villages in real life?

Check your answers on page 166. For full worked solutions see the CD.
See the Student Book on the CD if you need more help.

Question	1	2	3
Grade	D	D	D
Student Book pages	330–332	332–334	334–335

Ratio and proportion: topic test

Check how well you know this topic by answering these questions.
First cover the answers on the facing page.

Test questions

1 When ten people hire a boat for a weekend the cost per person is £56.
Work out the cost per person when the same boat is hired for a weekend by

(a) 5 people

(b) 7 people

(c) 8 people.

2 Kate is paid £100.80 for 16 hours' work in a café.
How much should she be paid for 12 hours' work?

3 The ingredients for making 15 cakes are:

250 g flour	175 g butter	175 g sugar
200 g fruit	3 eggs	330 ml milk

Jenny wants to make 10 of these cakes. Change the amounts given in the recipe to those needed for 10 cakes.
Give all your answers to the nearest whole unit.

4 Two towns are 7.5 cm apart on a map.
The scale of the map is 1 : 50 000
How far apart are the towns in real life?

5 Fatima has 35 CDs and DVDs.
The ratio of the number of CDs to the number of DVDs is 3 : 4
Work out how many CDs she has.

6 Given that 5 miles is equivalent to 8 kilometres

(a) work out, in kilometres
  (i) 40 miles   (ii) 12 miles   (iii) 240 miles

(b) work out, in miles
  (i) 24 kilometres   (ii) 50 kilometres   (iii) 3 kilometres

7 The depths of two wells are in the ratio 7 : 9
The depth of the deeper of the two wells is 63 metres.
Work out the depth of the other well.

Now check your answers – see the facing page.

Cover this page while you answer the test questions opposite.

Worked answers

Revise this on...

D **1** $10 \times £56 = £560$ for the hire of the boat — page 34
  (a) $£560 \div 5 = £112$ each for 5 people
  (b) $£560 \div 7 = £80$ each for 7 people
  (c) $£560 \div 8 = £70$ each for 8 people

D **2** 16 hours for £100.80 — page 34
  1 hour for $£100.80 \div 16 = £6.30$
  12 hours for $£6.30 \times 12 = £75.60$
  She should be paid £75.60 for 12 hours' work.

D **3** Ratio $15 : 10 = 3 : 2$ → Divide by 3 and multiply by 2 — page 34
  Flour $250 g \div 3 \times 2 = 167 g$ Butter $175 \div 3 \times 2 = 117 g$
  Sugar $175 \div 3 \times 2 = 117 g$ Fruit $200 \div 3 \times 2 = 133 g$
  Eggs $3 \div 3 \times 2 = 2$ eggs   Milk $330 \div 3 \times 2 = 220 ml$

D **4** $7.5 cm \times 50\,000 = 375\,000 cm$ — page 35
  $= 3750 m$ Divide by 100
  $= 3.75 km$ Divide by 1000

C **5** $3 + 4 = 7$ parts → $35 \div 7 = 5$ → $3 \times 5 = 15$ — page 33
  She has 15 CDs.

C **6** **(a)** 5 miles $= 8 km$ → 1 mile $= 8 km \div 5 = 1.6 km$ — page 34
    (i) $40 \times 1.6 = 64 km$ **(ii)** $12 \times 1.6 = 19.2 km$
    (iii) $240 \times 1.6 = 384 km$
  (b) 8 km $= 5$ miles → 1 km $= 5 \div 8 = 0.625$ miles
    (i) $24 \times 0.625 = 15$ miles   **(ii)** $50 \times 0.625 = 31.25$ miles
    (iii) $3 \times 0.625 = 1.875$ miles

C **7** Ratio of shallow to deep is $7 : 9$ — page 33
  9 'parts' $= 63 m$ → 1 'part' $= 7 m$ → 7 'parts' $= 7 \times 7 = 49 m$
  The shallower well is 49 m deep.

Tick the questions you got right.

Question	1	2	3	4	5	6	7
Grade	D	D	D	D	C	C	C

Mark the grade you are working at on your revision planner on page vii.

Number: subject test

Check how well you know this topic by answering these questions.

Exam practice questions

1 (a) Write 7432 in words.

    (b) Round 23 250 to the nearest thousand.

    (c) Write down the value of the 3 in 63 750

    (d) Write twenty-four thousand, five hundred and seventy-six in figures.

2 Work out these.

    (a) $2 + 6$

    (b) $-3 - 7$

    (c) -3×-2

3 (a) Work out 35% of £80

    (b) Simon buys a TV for £64 plus VAT at $17\frac{1}{2}$%
        Work out the total cost of the TV.

4 Rashmi buys 5 identical tins of paint for £35.
    Work out the cost of 8 of these tins of paint.

5 Work out these. Show all your working.

    (a) 246×43

    (b) $3.75 \div 0.15$

6 (a) Find the LCM of 24 and 36
    (b) Find the HCF of 24 and 36

7 **(a)** Estimate the answer to

$$\frac{299 \times 9.78}{21 \times 0.0199}$$

(b) Use your calculator to find the answer to

$$\frac{3.45^2 - \sqrt{11.5}}{4.56 + 2.05}$$

(c) Write your answer to part **(b)**

(i) to 2 decimal places

(ii) to 1 significant figure.

8 **(a)** Shade in $\frac{3}{4}$ of this rectangle.

(b) Work out $\frac{3}{4}$ of £36

(c) Write these fractions in order of size, smallest first:

$$\frac{2}{3}, \ \frac{3}{5}, \ \frac{3}{4}, \ \frac{1}{2}$$

(d) Work out $\frac{2}{3} - \frac{1}{4}$

(e) Work out $3\frac{3}{5} \times 2\frac{2}{9}$

9 Rachel shares £32 between her children Marco and José in the ratio 5 : 3
How much money does each child receive?

Check your answers on page 167. For full worked solutions see the CD.

Tick the questions you got right.

Question	1	2ab	2c	3a	3b	4	5a	5b	6	7a	7b	7ci	7cii	8a	8b	8c	8d	8e	9
Grade	G	F	E	E	D	D	E	C	C	D	C	F	E	G	F	E	D	C	C
Revise this on page	2–3	4	4	27	28	34	10	15	9	11, 14	7, 11	16	17	20	21	21	22	22–23	33

Mark the grade you are working at on your revision planner on page vii.

Go to the pages shown to revise for the ones you got wrong.

Number

Integers

- To write a number to the **nearest 10,** look at the **units digit**.
- To write a number to the **nearest 100**, look at the **tens digit**.
- To write a number to the **nearest 1000**, look at the **hundreds digit**.

If it is 5 or more, round up. If it is less than 5, round down.

- Adding a negative number has the same effect as subtracting the positive number:
  $$4 + -1 = 3$$
- Subtracting a negative number has the same effect as adding the positive number:
  $$2 - -3 = 5$$
- When multiplying or dividing two **like signs** give a $+$, two **unlike signs** give a $-$
- The **power** is how many times a number is multiplied by itself: $2 \times 2 \times 2 \times 2 = 2^4$. A power is also called an **index** (plural **indices**).
- To **multiply** powers of the same number, add the indices: $2^3 \times 2^4 = 2^{3+4} = 2^7$
- To **divide** powers of the same number, subtract the indices: $5^6 \div 5^4 = 5^{6-4} = 5^2$
- **BIDMAS** is a made-up word to help you remember the order of operations:

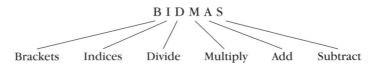

$$B\ I\ D\ M\ A\ S$$

Brackets   Indices   Divide   Multiply   Add   Subtract

- The **factors** of a number are whole numbers that divide exactly into the number.
  1, 2, 3, 4, 6 and 12 are factors of 12
- **Multiples** of a number are the results of multiplying the number by a positive whole number.
  3, 6 and 9 are multiples of 3
- A **prime number** is a number with only 2 factors, 1 and itself.
  1 is not a prime number as it can only be divided by one number (itself).
- To **estimate** the approximate answer to a calculation, round each number to **1 significant figure** (1 s.f.).

Decimals and rounding

- When you multiply decimals, work out the multiplication without the decimal points and put in the decimal point at the end.
- When dividing by decimals make sure you always divide by a whole number by multiplying both numbers by 10, 100 or 1000 etc. Make sure the decimal point in the answer lines up with the one in the question.
- To round to a given number of **decimal places (d.p.)**, count the number of decimal places and look at the next digit. If it is 5 or more, round up; if it is less than 5, round down.
- To round to a given number of **significant figures** (s.f.), count the number of digits from the first non-zero digit, starting from the *left*. Look at the next digit to decide whether to round up or down.

Fractions

- Top heavy fractions are called **improper fractions**.

- An improper fraction can be written as a **mixed number**, $\frac{12}{5} = 2\frac{2}{5}$.

- **Equivalent fractions** have the same value and can be cancelled down into their simplest terms:
  $$\frac{8}{12} = \frac{4}{6} = \frac{2}{3}.$$

- **Addition and subtraction**
  - You can only add and subtract fractions that have the same bottom number (denominator).
  - Start by dealing with any whole numbers.
  - Then find equivalent fractions with the same denominator for the fractions.
  - You can then add or subtract.

- **Multiplication and division**
  When you multiply fractions you write any mixed numbers as improper fractions. You then multiply the numerators and the denominators.
  When you divide fractions you write any mixed numbers as improper fractions. Then write down the first fraction, invert the second fraction and multiply.

Percentages

- To compare fractions, decimals and percentages you can change them all to percentages.

- To find a percentage of an amount you can: change the percentage to a fraction and multiply *or* change the percentage to a decimal and multiply *or* work from 10%.

- To **increase** a number by a percentage, you find the percentage of that number and then add this to the starting number. To **decrease** a number by a percentage, you find the percentage of that number and then subtract this from the starting number.

- To write one number as a percentage of another write the amounts as a fraction, convert the fraction to a decimal and then change the decimal to a percentage by multiplying by 100.

- A **price index** shows how the price of something changes over time. The index always starts at 100. An index greater than 100 shows a price rise, while an index less than 100 shows a price fall.

Ratio and proportion

- Simplifying ratios
  - To **simplify** a ratio you divide both its numbers by a common factor.
  - When a ratio cannot be simplified it is said to be in its **lowest terms**.
  - Two ratios are **equivalent** when they both simplify to the same ratio.

- To share an amount in a given ratio find the total of all the ratio numbers, then split the amount into fractions with a denominator that is the total.

- Two quantities are in **direct proportion** if their ratio stays the same when the quantities increase or decrease.

Simplifying algebra

- An **algebraic expression** is a collection of letters, symbols and numbers:

  $a + 3b - 2c$ is an algebraic expression.

  This is a **term**

Key words

algebraic expression ☐
term ☐
like terms ☐

- You can combine **like terms** by adding and subtracting them:

  $2a + 3a = 5a$ and $3b + 4b - b = 6b$

- You can simplify algebraic expressions by collecting like terms together:

  $2a - 4b + 3a + 5b$ simplifies to $5a + b$

Example   Simplify $3a + 5d + 2a + 6 - 3d - 8$

Grade E

$$3a + 5d + 2a + 6 - 3d - 8$$

Start by collecting like terms:
all the a terms, then
the d terms, then any $\longrightarrow$ $= 3a + 2a + 5d - 3d + 6 - 8$
separate numbers.

TIP
Keep each sign with its own term (no sign means $+$, so $3a$ is $+3a$). Here $5d$ is $+5d$, and the $3d$ term is $-3d$.

Add or subtract $\longrightarrow$ $=$ $5a$ $+2d$ -2
like terms. $= 5a + 2d - 2$

TIP
$+6 + -8 = -2$
For more on adding negative numbers see page 4.

WATCH OUT!
When collecting terms by adding or subtracting, the letter stays the same: $a + a = 2a$.
When you multiply, $a \times a = a^2$
Students sometimes wrongly write $3a + 2a$ as $5a^2$ or $6a^2$.

- The ^{2} in 7^2 is called an **index** or **power**. It tells you how many times the given number must be multiplied by itself.

Key words

power ☐
index ☐

- To **multiply** powers of the same number or letter, add the indices:

  $3^3 \times 3^4 = 3^{3+4} = 3^7$ $x^a \times x^b = x^{a+b}$

- To **divide** powers of the same number or letter, subtract the indices:

  $4^5 \div 4^2 = 4^{5-2} = 4^3$ $x^a \div x^b = x^{a-b}$

TIP
These are called the index laws.

- Any number or letter raised to the **power 1** is equal to the number or letter itself:

  $3^1 = 3$ $x^1 = x$

- Any non-zero number or letter raised to the **power 0** is equal to 1:

  $3^0 = 1$ $y^0 = 1$

Example — Simplify $6y^6 \div 3y^2$

Method 1: Using the index laws

$$6y^6 \div 3y^2$$

Divide the numbers. ———• $6 \div 3 = 2$

TIP
$x^a \div x^b = x^{a-b}$

Divide the letter terms. ———• $y^6 \div y^2 = y^{6-2} = y^4$

Combine the number and letter parts.—• $6y^6 \div 3y^2 = 2y^4$

Method 2

$$6y^6 \div 3y^2$$

Write the division like this. ———• $= \dfrac{6y^6}{3y^2} = \dfrac{6}{3} \times \dfrac{y \times y \times y \times y \times y \times y}{y \times y}$

TIP
6 and 3 have common factor 3, so cancel by 3. Two of the ys in the denominator cancel with two of the ys in the numerator.

Look for common factors and cancel.—• $= \dfrac{2}{1} \times \dfrac{\cancel{y} \times \cancel{y} \times y \times y \times y \times y}{\cancel{y} \times \cancel{y}}$

Write the answer as simply as possible. → $= 2 \times y \times y \times y \times y$
$= 2 \times y^4$
$= 2y^4$

TIP
$\dfrac{2}{1} = 2$

Practice

1 Simplify **(a)** $e + e + c + e + e$ **(b)** $3 \times j \times k$

2 Simplify **(a)** $5a + 4b + 3a - 3b$ **(b)** $p^3 + p^3 + p^3 + p^3$

3 Simplify **(a)** $3p \times 5q$ **(b)** $t \times t \times t$

4 Simplify **(a)** $h^3 \times h^4$ **(b)** $\dfrac{12x^5}{3x^2}$

Check your answers on page 167. For full worked solutions see the CD.
See the Student Book on the CD if you need more help.

Question	1	2	3	4
Grade	F	E	D	C
Student Book pages	47–48, 50–51	48–50, 78–80	50–51, 55–56	52, 56–57

Expanding brackets and factorising

- You can combine **like terms** by adding or subtracting them:

    $2a + 3a = 5a$ and $3b + 4b - b = 6b$

- You can simplify algebraic expressions by collecting like terms together:

    $2a - 4b + 3a + 5b$ simplifies to $5a + b$

- **Expanding** the brackets means multiplying to remove the brackets.

Key words

like terms ☐
expand ☐

Example   Expand $3(x + 5)$

Grade D

Multiply each term inside the bracket ⟶ $3(x + 5) = \mathbf{3} \times x + \mathbf{3} \times 5$
by the term outside the bracket. $= 3x + 15$

Example   Expand $x(m - 2)$

Grade D

Multiply each term inside the bracket ⟶ $\mathbf{x}(m - 2) = \mathbf{x} \times m + \mathbf{x} \times -2$
by the term outside the bracket. $= mx - 2x$

TIP
Write the letters in alphabetical order.

WATCH OUT!
Don't forget the negative sign.

Example   Simplify $5(a + 2b) - 2(2a - 5b)$

Grade C

$$\mathbf{5}(a + 2b) - \mathbf{2}(2a - 5b)$$

Multiply each term inside ⟶ $= \mathbf{5} \times a + \mathbf{5} \times +2b - \mathbf{2} \times +2a - \mathbf{2} \times -5b$
the bracket by the term $= 5a + 10b - 4a + 10b$
outside the bracket.

Collect like terms together: ⟶ $= 5a - 4a + 10b + 10b$
all the a terms,
then the b terms.

Add or subtract the ⟶ $=\quad a \quad + \quad 20b$
like terms. $= a + 20b$

TIP
A minus term outside the bracket multiplying a minus term inside the bracket gives $- \times - = +$
Here $-2 \times -5 = +10$
For more on multiplying negative numbers see page 4.

WATCH OUT!
Make sure you multiply *every* term inside the bracket by the term outside. Students often wrongly expand $5(a + 2b)$ to give $5a + 2b$ instead of the correct expansion $5a + 10b$.

- **Factorising** means splitting up an expression using brackets:

$$12a + 4b = 4(3a + b)$$

Example

Factorise $3x^2 - 6x$

Find all the common factors of both terms. → $3x^2 - 6x$
3 and x are common factors.

EXAMINER'S TIP

You need to factorise *fully* to get full marks.

Write the highest common factor outside the bracket. → $= 3x(\quad)$

WATCH OUT!

To factorise fully, make sure you have the *highest* common factor outside the bracket. Students often wrongly use only one factor, obtaining either $3(x^2 - 2x)$ or $x(3x - 6)$.

Work out what is needed inside the bracket. → $= 3x(x - 2)$

TIP

You can check your answer by expanding:
$3x(x - 2) = 3x^2 - 6x$

Practice

1 Expand
- (a) $2(c + 6)$
- (b) $d(a - 3)$
- (c) $b(b + 2)$

2 Expand and simplify
- (a) $2(5p - 3) + 4(3p + 2)$
- (b) $5(3g + 2h) - 3(4g - h)$
- (c) $4p + 3(p + 2)$

3 Factorise
- (a) $3c + 12$
- (b) $4m^2 - 12m$
- (c) $2t^2 - 6t$

Check your answers on page 167. For full worked solutions see the CD.
See the Student Book on the CD if you need more help.

Question	1	2	3
Grade	D	C	C
Student Book pages	60, 63	61–63	64–65

Manipulative algebra: topic test

Check how well you know this topic by answering these questions.
First cover the answers on the facing page.

Test questions

1 Simplify $t + t + t$

2 Simplify $3 \times c \times d$

3 Simplify $6g - 4g$

4 Simplify $2y + 2y + 2y$

5 Simplify $\dfrac{12x}{3}$

6 Simplify $7x + 3y - 2x + y$

7 Simplify $x^2 + x^2 + x^2$

8 Simplify $p \times p \times p \times p$

9 Expand $3(k - 2)$

10 Expand $4(2a - 3b)$

11 Simplify $d^3 \times d^5$

12 Simplify $3y^5 \div y^2$

13 Expand and simplify $3(2a + b) + 2(a - b)$

14 Expand and simplify $3(2x + 4) - 5(3 - x)$

15 Expand $2a(a + b)$

16 Expand $x(2x^2 + 1)$

17 Factorise $4a + 8$

18 Factorise $3m^2 - 6m$

Now check your answers – see the facing page.

Cover this page while you answer the test questions opposite.

Worked answers

Revise this on...

F   **1** $t + t + t = 3t$ page 42

F   **2** $3 \times c \times d = 3cd$ page 43

F   **3** $6g - 4g = 2g$ page 42

F   **4** $2y + 2y + 2y = y + y + y + y + y + y = 6y$ page 42

F   **5** $\frac{12x}{3} = 12x \div 3 = 4x$ page 43

E   **6** $7x + 3y - 2x + y = 7x - 2x + 3y + y = 5x + 4y$ page 42

E   **7** $x^2 + x^2 + x^2 = 3x^2$ page 43

D   **8** $p \times p \times p \times p = p^4$ page 43

D   **9** $3(k - 2) = 3 \times k + 3 \times -2 = 3k - 6$ page 44

D   **10** $4(2a - 3b) = 4 \times 2a + 4 \times -3b = 8a - 12b$ page 44

C   **11** $d^3 \times d^5 = d^{3+5} = d^8$ pages 42–43

C   **12** $3y^5 \div y^2 = 3y^{5-2} = 3y^3$ pages 42–43

C   **13** $3(2a + b) + 2(a - b) = 6a + 3b + 2a - 2b = 8a + b$ page 44

C   **14** $3(2x + 4) - 5(3 - x) = 6x + 12 - 15 + 5x = 6x + 5x + 12 - 15 = 11x - 3$ page 44

C   **15** $2a(a + b) = 2a \times a + 2a \times b = 2a^2 + 2ab$ page 44

C   **16** $x(2x^2 + 1) = x \times 2x^2 + x \times 1 = 2x^3 + x$ page 44

C   **17**   The common factor is 4, so $4a + 8 = 4(a + 2)$ page 45

C   **18**   The common factor is 3m, so $3m^2 - 6m = 3m(m - 2)$ page 45

Tick the questions you got right.

Question	1	2	3	4	5	6	7	8	9	10	11	12	13	14	15	16	17	18
Grade	F	F	F	F	F	E	E	D	D	D	C	C	C	C	C	C	C	C

Mark the grade you are working at on your revision planner on page vii.

Number sequences

- In a **number pattern** or **sequence** there is always a **rule** to get from one number to the next. For example:

1, 4, 7, 10, …	The rule is: add 3
50, 46, 42, 38, …	The rule is: take away 4
2, 4, 8, 16, …	The rule is: multiply by 2

- To find the rule for the *n*th **term** of a number pattern, use a table of values. For example:

Term number	1	2	3	4
Term	1	4	7	10
Difference		+3	+3	+3

The rule is 'add 3' so the number in front of the *n* is 3. The rule starts with 3*n*.
Look at the first term, *n* = 1, to find the number to add or subtract.

Example

This is part of a sequence of numbers: 2, 8, __ , __ , 26
(a) Find the missing numbers.
(b) Write down the general rule, in terms of *n*, for the *n*th term of the sequence.

Grade F

Grade C

Find the number differences. ⟶ (a) 2   8   __   __   26

             +6   +6   +6   +6

Use the difference to work out ⟶   8 + 6 = 14, then 14 + 6 = 20
the missing numbers.

> **TIP**
> Check that your rule gives the next term correctly:
> 20 + 6 = 6

Use the differences to write the ⟶ (b) The differences are +6, so the first part of
first part of the rule.   the rule is 6n

Look at the first term, ⟶   6n = 6 × 1 = 6
when *n* = 1.   You need to subtract 4 to get the first term: 6 − 4 = 2

Write the rule. ⟶   6n − 4

Example

Here is a pattern made from sticks:

    Diagram 1   Diagram 2   Diagram 3

Grade G

(a) Draw Diagram 4.

(b) Complete the table.

Diagram	1	2	3	4	5
Number of sticks	5	9	13		

Grade G

(c) Write down a formula for the number of sticks, *S*, in terms of the pattern number, *n*.

Grade C

Look at how the pattern grows. → (a)

Draw the next one in the sequence.

Diagram 4

Write down the numbers of → (b) 5   9   13

sticks and their
differences to help find
the next two numbers.

+4   +4

$13 + 4 = 17$, and $17 + 4 = 21$

TIP

The differences are +4,
so the first part is 4n

Use the differences to write → (c) 4n

the first part of the rule.

$4n = 4 \times 1 = 4$

Look at the first term, when $n = 1$.

You need to add 1 to get
the first term: $4 + 1 = 5$

WATCH OUT!

Remember to look back at
the numbers in the sequence
to see if your formula works.
Students often wrongly write
the rule as n + 4, or 4n

Write the formula, as that is →
what the question asks for.

The formula is $S = 4n + 1$

EXAMINER'S TIP

If the question asks for the *rule*, this is 4n + 1.
If the question asks for a *formula*, it needs an equals sign.

Practice

1   Here is a pattern made from dots:

Diagram 1   Diagram 2   Diagram 3

Grade G

(a) Draw Diagram 4

Grade F

(c) Write down a rule to work
out the number of dots in
the 15th diagram.

(b) Complete the table.

Diagram	1	2	3	4	5
Number of dots	7	10	13		

(d) Find a rule for the number of dots, in
terms of n, in the nth diagram.

Grade G

Grade C

2   Here is a sequence of numbers: 30, 26, __ , __ , 14, 10

Find the missing terms in this sequence of numbers.

Grade F

3   Here is number sequence: 4, 11, 18, 25, 32

Find a rule, in terms of n, for the nth term of this sequence.

Grade C

Check your answers on page 167. For full worked solutions see the CD.
See the student book on the CD if you need more help.

Question	1ab	1c	1d	2	3
Grade	G	F	C	F	C
Student Book pages	72–75		73–75	67–71	73–75

Patterns and sequences: topic test

Check how well you know this topic by answering these questions.
First cover the answers on the facing page.

Test questions

1   This is a series of diagrams made from sticks.

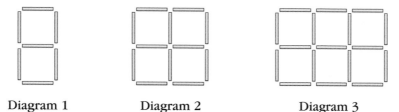

Diagram 1   Diagram 2   Diagram 3

(a)   Draw Diagram 4.

(b)   Complete the table.

Diagram	1	2	3	4	5
Number of sticks	7	12	17		

(c)   Write down a rule to find the number of sticks in the 10th diagram.

(d)   Find the general rule for the number of sticks in the nth diagram.

2   These numbers are part of a number sequence:

      5, 8, 6, 9, 7, 10, 8, …

(a) Write down the next two numbers in the sequence.

(b) Explain how you found your numbers.

3   These numbers are part of a sequence:

      1, 5, 9, 13, 17, …

Write down the general rule, in terms of n, for the nth term in the sequence.

Now check your answers – see the facing page.

Cover this page while you answer the test questions opposite.

Worked answers

Revise this on...

G   **1**   (a)   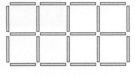   pages 48–49

A column is ↑
added each time.   Diagram 4

G   (b)   7   12   17   pages 48–49

+5   +5

5 sticks are added for each extra column.
So 17 + 5 = 22   for Diagram 4
    22 + 5 = 27   for Diagram 5

F   (c)   7   12   17   22   27   pages 48–49
1st diagram = 1 × 5 + 2 = 7
2nd diagram = 2 × 5 + 2 = 12
3rd diagram = 3 × 5 + 2 = 17
so
10th diagram = 10 × 5 + 2 = 52

C   (d)   In words the rule is 'Multiply the diagram number by 5, and add 2'   pages 48–49
In terms of n, the rule is 5n + 2

F   **2**   (a)   5   8   6   9   7   10   8   page 48

+3   −2   +3   −2   +3   −2

(b)   The differences are +3, then −2.
So the next two numbers are: 8 + 3 = 11, then 11 − 2 = 9

C   **3**   1   5   9   13   17   page 48

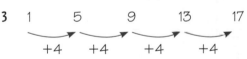

+4   +4   +4   +4

The differences are +4, so the first part of the general rule is 4n.
For the first term, n = 1:   4n = 4 × 1 = 4
You need to subtract 3 to get the first number in the sequence: 4 − 3 = 1
The general rule is 4n − 3.

Tick the questions you got right.

Question	1ab	1c	1d	2	3
Grade	G	F	C	F	C

Mark the grade you are working at on your revision planner on page vii.

Coordinates

- The number line is **1-dimensional** or **1-D**. You can describe positions on the number line using one number or **coordinate**, for example (2).

- Flat shapes are **2-dimensional** or **2-D**. You can describe positions on a flat shape using two numbers or coordinates, for example (2, 1).

Key words

1-dimensional ☐
2-dimensional ☐
coordinates ☐

axis ☐
mid-point ☐

Example

(a) Write down the coordinates of
   (i) point A (ii) point B.

(b) Plot these points on the grid.
   (i) $C(2, 3)$
   (ii) $D(-2, 0)$
   (iii) $E(-2, -1)$

(c) Write down the coordinates of the **mid-point** of the line FG.

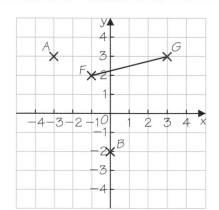

Grade F

Grade F

Grade D

To find the coordinates:
   Read the number on the x-axis.
   Read the number on the y-axis.

(a) (i) Point A is $(-3, 3)$
   (ii) Point B is $(0, -2)$

WATCH OUT!

Write x before y. Students often wrongly put the y-coordinate first.

The x-coordinate tells you how far to go along the x-axis.
The y-coordinate tells you how far to go up or down.

(b)

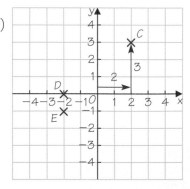

Write down the coordinates of the end-points.

(c) F is $(-1, 2)$ and G is $(3, 3)$

To find the coordinates of the mid-point:

   Add the x-coordinates and divide by 2. $\dfrac{-1 + 3}{2} = \dfrac{2}{2} = 1$

   Add the y-coordinates and divide by 2. $\dfrac{2 + 3}{2} = \dfrac{5}{2} = 2\frac{1}{2}$

The coordinates of the mid-point are $(1, 2\frac{1}{2})$.

- Solid shapes are **3-dimensional** or **3-D**. You can describe positions in a solid shape using three numbers or coordinates, for example (4, 1, 2).

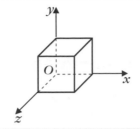

Key words

3-D coordinate ☐
3-dimensional ☐

Example

Grade C

Write down the coordinates of points A, B, C and D.

Read off the values from the x-axis, the y-axis, and the z-axis.

A is (0, 3, 2)
B is (0, 0, 2)
C is (2, 0, 2)
D is (2, 3, 0)

TIP

Start at O. To get to A you go 0 units along the x-axis, +3 along the y-axis and +2 along the z-axis.

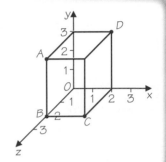

Practice

Grade G

1 Write down the coordinates of

(a) point A   (b) point B.

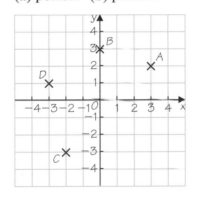

2 Write down the coordinates of

(a) point C   (b) point D.

Grade F

3 Write down the coordinates of the mid-point of the line PQ.

Grade D

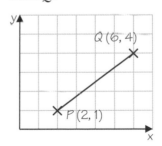

Grade C

4 Write down the coordinates of points K, L, M and N.

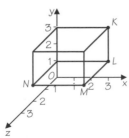

Check your answers on page 167.
For full worked solutions see the CD.
See the Student Book on the CD if you need more help.

Question	1	2	3	4
Grade	G	F	D	C
Student Book pages	299–300	312	300–301	316–318

Linear graphs

- A graph representing a **linear relationship** is always a straight line.

- **Distance–time graphs** are used to relate the distance travelled to the time taken, and to calculate speeds.

Key words

time ☐   distance–time graph ☐
distance ☐   average speed ☐

Example

The distance–time graph represents a cyclist's journey.

(a) At what time did the cyclist take a break?

(b) Why does the graph slope downwards after 6 pm?

(c) How far from home was the cyclist at 5 pm?

(d) What was the cyclist's average speed between 1 pm and 3 pm?

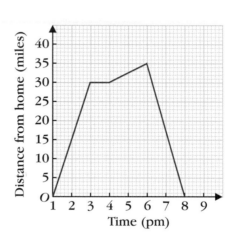

Grade E

Grade E

Grade E

Grade D

A horizontal line represents no movement. ⟶ (a) Break from 3 pm to 4 pm

> **TIP**
> Time is shown on the horizontal axis.

A downward slope means the distance from the starting point is decreasing. ⟶ (b) The cyclist is travelling back towards home.

> **TIP**
> The vertical distance on the graph is the distance from home.

Draw a vertical line up to the graph and across to the distance axis. ⟶ (c) $32\frac{1}{2}$ miles

Work out the total distance. ⟶ (d) From 1 pm to 3 pm the cyclist travels 30 miles.

> **TIP**
> Read the scale carefully. Half way between 30 and 35 is $32\frac{1}{2}$ miles.

Work out the total time. ⟶ 1 pm to 3 pm = 2 hours

Speed = distance ÷ time. ⟶ Speed = 30 miles in 2 hours
= 15 miles in 1 hour
So speed is 15 mph

> **TIP**
> Speed in mph is the distance travelled in 1 hour.

Practice

1 The graph represents a saleswoman's journey to and from a meeting.

(a) How long did the meeting last?

Grade E

(b) How far had the saleswoman travelled after 1 hour?

Grade E

(c) What was her average speed from $2\frac{1}{2}$ hours to 3 hours?

Grade D

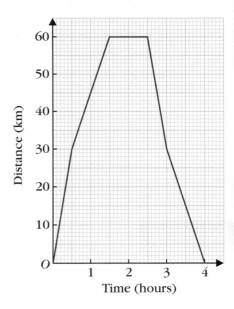

2 The graph represents the movement of a remote control car, to and from a starting point.

(a) How far from the starting point did the car travel?

Grade E

(b) For how long was the car stationary?

Grade E

(c) What was the average speed of the car, in metres per second, during the first 10 seconds?

Grade D

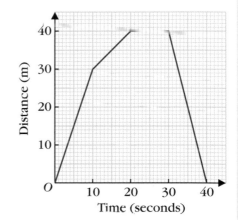

3 The graph shows part of Alison's journey to visit her grandmother.

(a) What was Alison's speed between 13:00 and 14:00?

(b) Alison travels home at an average speed of 40 km/h.
Complete the travel graph.

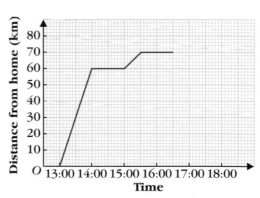

Check your answers on page 167. For full worked solutions see the CD.

See the Student Book on the CD if you need more help.

Question	1ab	1c	2ab	2c	3
Grade	E	D	E	D	C
Student Book pages	306–309		306–309		306–309

Algebraic line graphs

- The **equation of a line** uses algebra to show a relationship between the x- and y-coordinates of points on the line.

- An equation containing an x-term and no higher powers of x (such as x^2) is a **linear equation**.

- The graph of a linear equation is a straight line.

Example

Grade E

(a) Complete the table of values for $y = 3x - 1$.

x	-2	-1	0	1	2	3
y						

(b) Use your table of values to draw the graph of $y = 3x - 1$.

(c) Use your graph to find

    (i)   the value of y when $x = 1.5$

    (ii) the value of x when $y = 6.5$

Work out each value of y. ●————

(a) When x = **3**, y = 3 × **3** − 1 = 8
When x = **2**, y = 3 × **2** − 1 = 5
When x = **1**, y = 3 × **1** − 1 = 2

> **TIP**
>
> Start working out the values from the right-hand (positive) side of the table. Try to spot the pattern in the numbers in the table: this will help you complete it. Here the pattern is −3 each time (from right to left).

x	−2	−1	0	1	2	3
y	−7	−4	−1	2	5	8

This represents the point $(-2, -7)$

Plot the table values on the grid. ●———— (b)

> **WATCH OUT!**
>
> y = 3x − 1 is a linear equation. If the points do not join to give a single straight line you have made an error: check your working.

Join the points with a single straight line.

Draw a line from the x-value ●———— up to the line and across to the y-axis.

(c) (i) When x = 1.5, y = 3.5

Draw a line from the y-value ●———— across to the line and down to the x-axis.

(ii) When y = 6.5, x = 2.5

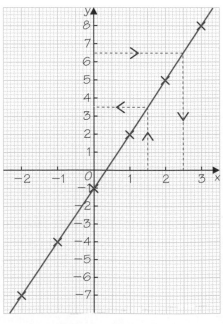

Example

(a) Write down the equation of the line *AB*.

(b) On a copy of the grid, draw the line

   (i) $x = 3$ (ii) $y = -2$

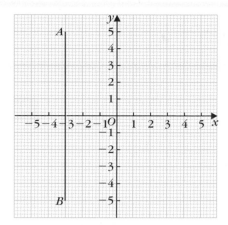

Look at the coordinates of different points on the line. ──────•

(a) Any point on the line AB has x-coordinate −3.

▼

Try to spot a pattern. ──────•

The equation of the line is x = −3

What does the equation tell you about the coordinates? ──────•

(b) (i) On the line x = 3 all points must have x-coordinate 3

▼

Plot a few points with x-coordinate 3 and join them with a straight line.

(ii) On the line y = −2, all points must have y-coordinate −2

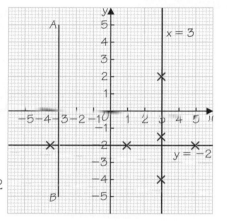

Practice

1 On the grid, draw the line

   (a) $y = 2$ (b) $x = -4$

2 (a) Complete the table of values for $y = \frac{1}{2}x + 1$.

x	−4	−3	−2	−1	0	1	2
y							

(b) Draw the graph of $y = \frac{1}{2}x + 1$ on the grid.

(c) Use your graph to find
   (i) the value of y when $x = \frac{1}{2}$
   (ii) the value of x when $y = -\frac{3}{4}$

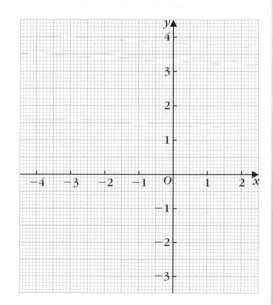

Check your answers on page 167. For full worked solutions see the CD.

See the Student Book on the CD if you need more help.

Question	1	2
Grade	F	E
Student Book pages	313–314	314–316

Curved graphs

- An equation containing an x^2-term is called a **quadratic equation**.

- The graph of a quadratic equation is a curved quadratic graph, or parabola. It has a symmetrical U- shape: $\cup$ or $\cap$.

Key words

| curve ☐ | quadratic ☐ |
| equation ☐ | coordinate ☐ |

Example

Grade C

(a) Complete the table of values for $y = 3x^2 - 3x - 2$.

x	-2	-1	0	1	2	3
y						

(b) On the grid, use your table of values to draw the graph of $y = 3x^2 - 3x - 2$.

(c) Write down the minimum value of y.

(d) Use your graph to find

   (i) the value of y when $x = 1.8$

   (ii) the values of x when $y = 6$

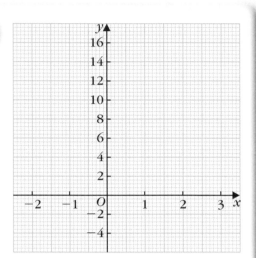

$y = 3x^2 - 3x - 2$ is a quadratic graph, a curve.
Work out each value of y.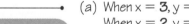

(a) When $x = \mathbf{3}$, $y = 3 \times \mathbf{3}^2 - 3 \times \mathbf{3} - 2 = 27 - 9 - 2 = 16$
When $x = \mathbf{2}$, $y = 3 \times \mathbf{2}^2 - 3 \times \mathbf{2} - 2 = 12 - 6 - 2 = 4$

TIP

Start working out the values from the right-hand (positive) side of the table. Try to spot symmetry in the numbers in the table: this will help you complete it.

x	-2	-1	0	1	2	3
y	16	4	-2	-2	4	16

This means the point $(-2, 16)$

Plot the table values on the grid.

(b)

WATCH OUT!

The bottom must be curved. If there are two points at the bottom the curve should sink slightly below them. Students often wrongly draw a straight line.

Join the points with a curve.

The minimum value of y is at the bottom of the curve. Draw a line across to the y-axis.

(c) $y = -2.7$

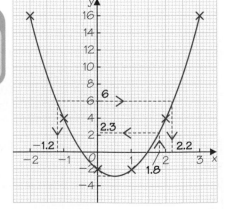

Draw a line from the x-value up to the line and across to the y-axis.

(d) (i) When $x = 1.8$, $y = 2.3$

Draw a line from the y-value across to the line and down to the x-axis.

(ii) When $y = 6$, $x = -1.2$ and $x = 2.2$

Example

Water is poured into this container. Sketch a graph to show the relationship between the water level and the volume of water in the container.

Think about how the level of water increases in the different sections of the container.

▼

The water level rises at a steady rate when the walls of the container are vertical (*A* to *B*).

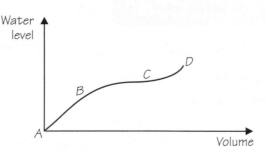

TIP
A steady increase is represented by a straight line.

When the container widens the water level rises more slowly (*B* to *C*).

When the container narrows the water level rises more quickly (*C* to *D*).

Practice

Grade C   **1**   **(a)** Complete the table of values for $y = x^2 - 3x$.

x	-1	0	1	2	3	4
y						

(b) Draw the graph of $y = x^2 - 3x$ on a copy of the grid.

(c) Use your graph to find

   (i) the value of y when $x = -\frac{1}{2}$

   (ii) the value of x when $y = 1.75$

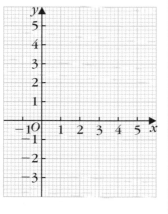

Grade C   **2**   The sketch graph shows the sound level of a television from when it is switched on. Describe how the sound level changes between

(a) *A* and *B*

(b) *B* and *C*

(c) *C* and *D*.

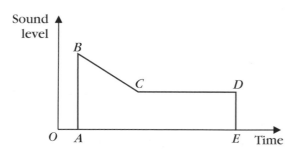

Check your answers on page 168. For full worked solutions see the CD.
See the Student Book on the CD if you need more help.

Question	1	2
Grade	C	C
Student Book pages	528–531	535–539

Coordinates and graphs: topic test

Check how well you know this topic by answering these questions.
First cover the answers on the facing page.

Test questions

1 This graph shows a car's journey.

    (a) How far is the car from home after 10 minutes?

    (b) For how long was the car stationary
    after 25 minutes?

    (c) What was the average speed, in km/h,
    from 15 minutes to 25 minutes?

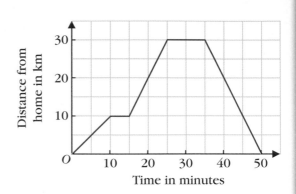

2 **(a)** Complete the table of values for $y = 2x - 3$.

x	-1	0	1	2	3	4
y						

    (b) On a copy of the grid, draw the graph of $y = 2x - 3$.

    (c) Use your graph to find the value of x when $y = 1.4$

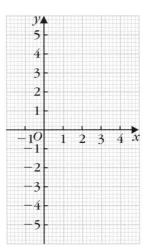

3 **(a)** Complete the table of values for $y = x^2 - 3x - 1$.

x	-1	0	1	2	3	4
y						

    (b) On a copy of the grid, draw the graph of $y = x^2 - 3x - 1$.

    (c) Use your graph to find the values of x when $y = 0.6$

4 Write down the coordinates of point M.

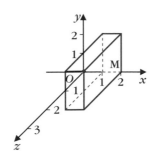

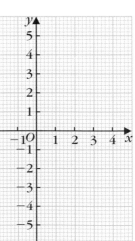

Now check your answers – see the facing page.

Cover this page while you answer the test questions opposite.

Worked answers

Revise this on...

E 1 **(a)** 10 km page 54

E **(b)** From 25 minutes the graph is horizontal for 2 divisions. page 54
Each division represents 5 minutes so the car is stationary for 10 minutes.

D **(c)** Between 15 minutes and 25 minutes the car travels 20 km. page 54
Speed = 20 km in 10 minutes
= 2 km per minute
= 120 km per hour

E 2 **(a)** When x = **4**, y = 2 × **4** − 3 = 5, page 56
when x = **3**, y = 2 × **3** − 3 = 3,
when x = **2**, y = 2 × **2** − 3 = 1, ...

x	−1	0	1	2	3	4
y	−5	−3	−1	1	3	5

(b) See graph below.
(c) From the graph (see below), when y = 1.4, x = 2.2

C 3 **(a)** When x = **4**, y = **4**² − 3 × **4** − 1 = 16 − 12 − 1 = 3, page 58
when x = **3**, y = **3**² − 3 × **3** − 1 = 9 − 9 − 1 = −1,
when x = **2**, y = **2**² − 3 × **2** − 1 = 4 − 6 − 1 = −3, ...

x	−1	0	1	2	3	4
y	3	−1	−3	−3	−1	3

(b) page 58

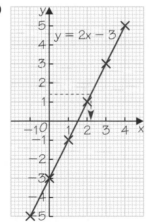

(c) From the graph, when y = 0.6, x = −0.5 and x = 3.5 page 58

C 4 The coordinates of point M are (2, 0, 0) page 53

Tick the questions you got right.

Question	1ab	1c	2	3	4
Grade	E	D	E	C	C

Mark the grade you are working at on your revision planner on page viii.

Formulae

- A **word formula** uses words to represent a relationship between quantities. For example:

  pay = rate of pay × hours worked

- An **algebraic formula** uses letters to represent a relationship between quantities. For example, the perimeter of a rectangle, P, is related to its length l and width w by

  $P = 2l + 2w$

Key words

formula ☐	word formula ☐
expression ☐	algebraic formula ☐

Example

The monthly charge for using a photocopier is given by the formula

$C = 0.05 × n + 80$

where C is the total charge, in £, and n is the number of photocopies made. Find the total cost for January, when 2200 photocopies were made.

Grade F

Identify the numbers to use in the formula. ⟶ To find C, you need n = 2200

▼

Write down the calculation. ⟶ C = 0.05 × n + 80

▼

Replace n with its number value. ⟶

= 0.05 × 2200 + 80
= 110 + 80
= £190

Example

The lengths of the sides of a triangle are shown in the diagram.

(a) Write down an expression in terms of x for the length of the perimeter.

(b) Write down a formula for the perimeter, P, in terms of x.

Grade D

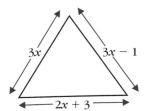

Think of the expression in words. ⟶ (a) Perimeter is the total of the lengths of all the sides of the triangle.
Write down the lengths of all the sides.
3x + 3x − 1 + 2x + 3

You need a formula for P, so write P ⟶ (b) P =
on the left of the equals sign.

TIP

A formula has two sides. The subject of the formula (what you are trying to find) is on the left of the equals sign, and how you find it is on the right.

On the right of the equals sign write how you work it out (the sum of the side lengths).

$P = 3x + 3x - 1 + 2x + 3$

Simplify by collecting like terms. ⟶ $= 8x + 2$

Example

C is the total cost in pounds of buying n CDs at £12 each. Write down a formula for C in terms of n.

Grade E

Think about the cost of different numbers of CDs. ⟶ Cost of 1 CD is £12
Cost of 2 CDs is 2 × £12

What is the cost of n CDs? ————— Cost of n CDs is n × 12

Write your formula using letters. ————— $C = n × 12$

Rewrite using correct algebraic notation (no × sign, numbers *before* letters). ————— $C = 12n$

TIP
Write the number first than the letter without the × sign.

Practice

1 The total number of eggs in some boxes is given by the formula

total number of eggs = 12 × number of boxes

Find the number of eggs in 15 boxes.

Grade F

2 The charge &C for parking in an airport car park is given by the formula
$C = 2h + 3$
where h is the number of hours.
Calculate the charge for parking a car for 4 hours.

Grade E

3 The weight of one computer is 8 kg, and the weight of its packaging is k kg.
Altogether, n computers are sold. The total weight of computers and packaging is W.
Write down a formula for W in terms of k and n.

Grade E

4 The lengths of the sides of a quadrilateral are shown in the diagram.
Write down a formula for the perimeter, P, in terms of y.

Grade C

$3y$
$3y + 4$
$3y - 2$
$4y + 1$

Check your answers on page 168. For full worked solutions see the CD.

See the Student Book on the CD if you need more help.

Question	1	2	3	4
Grade	F	E	E	C
Student Book pages	391–393	391–393	394	394

Rearranging formulae

- The **subject** of a **formula** appears on its own on one side of the formula and does not appear on the other side. For example:

$$t = 4l + 4 \text{ can be } \textbf{rearranged} \text{ to give } l = \frac{t-4}{4}$$

t is the subject	l is the subject

Key words

rearrange ☐
subject ☐
algebraic formula ☐

Example   Rearrange the formula $y = 6x + 2$ to make x the subject.

Grade D

Method 1

Draw a flowchart for the formula. ——●   x goes in → ☐×6☐ ☐+2☐ → y comes out

▼

Reverse the flowchart. ——●   x comes out ← ☐÷6☐ ☐−2☐ ← y goes in

$$\frac{y-2}{6} \longleftarrow y-2 \longleftarrow y$$

▼

Write down the algebraic formula. ——●   So $x = \dfrac{y-2}{6}$

Method 2

$$y = 6x + 2$$

Subtract 2 from both sides. ——● $y - 2 = 6x$

▼

Divide both sides by 6. ——● $\dfrac{y-2}{6} = x \qquad x = \dfrac{y-2}{6}$

Example   Rearrange the formula $a = 3x - cb$ to make x the subject.

Grade C

Draw a flowchart for the formula. ——●   x goes in → ☐×3☐ ☐−cb☐ → a comes out

$$x \longrightarrow 3x \longrightarrow 3x - cb$$

▼

Reverse the flowchart. ——●   x comes out ← ☐÷3☐ ☐+cb☐ ← a goes in

$$\frac{a+cb}{3} \longleftarrow a+cb \longleftarrow a$$

Write down the algebraic formula. ——●   So $x = \dfrac{a+cb}{3}$

TIP

The inverse of + is − and vice versa; the inverse of × is ÷ and vice versa.

- You can **substitute** numbers into formulae. 'Substitute' means 'replace a letter with a number value.'

Example

Given the formula $P = bc + 8$
(a) find P when $b = -2$ and $c = 3$
(b) find b when $P = 20$ and $c = 4$.

Grade C

Substitute the numbers for the letters. ⟶●

(a) $P = bc + 8$
$P = -2 \times 3 + 8$

WATCH OUT!
Remember that bc means b × c. Here bc = −2 × 3. Students often wrongly write bc as −23

Work out in the correct order. ⟶●

$= -6 + 8$
$= 2$

Substitute the numbers for the letters. ⟶●

(b) $P = bc + 8$
$20 = b \times 4 + 8$
$20 = 4b + 8$

Now rearrange to make b the subject. ⟶●

$12 = 4b$ Subtract 8 from both sides
$3 = b$ Divide both sides by 4
So $b = 3$

Practice

1. (a) Using the formula $x = ab + c$, find the value of x when $a = 0.6$, $b = 10$ and $c - -2$.
   (b) Using the formula $y = 2c + d$, find the value of y when $c = 0.8$ and $d - -2$.

Grade D

2. (a) Rearrange $3x - 4 = y$ to make x the subject.
   (b) Rearrange $2x + 3 = y$ to make x the subject.

Grade D

3. (a) Rearrange $4x + bc = a$ to make x the subject.
   (b) Rearrange $2(x + 3) = t$ to make x the subject.

Grade C

4. Given the formula $v = u + at$, find the value of a when $v = 21.5$, $u = 4$ and $t = 7$.

Grade C

Check your answers on page 168. For full worked solutions see the CD.
See the Student Book on the CD if you need more help.

Question	1	2	3	4
Grade	D	D	C	C
Student Book pages	394–399	539–541	539–541	399–400

Formulae: topic test

Check how well you know this topic by answering these questions.
First cover the answers on the facing page.

Test questions

1 The total cost of buying a number of pencils is given by the word formula

total cost = number of pencils × cost of each pencil

Find the total cost when the number of pencils is 15 and the cost of each pencil is 8p.

2 The total cost of hiring a piece of equipment is given by the formula

total cost = number of hours × £15 + £30

Find the total cost of hiring a piece of equipment for 8 hours.

3 $T = 2p + 3q$ Find T when $p = 4$ and $q = 5$.

4 C is the total cost of buying n books at £8 each.
Write down a formula for the total cost of buying n books.

5 $H = 7c - 3d$ Find H when $c = 2$ and $d = -3$.

6 $y = 4x - 3$ Find x when $y = 7$.

7 Pens cost 20p each and pencils cost 15p each.
T is the total cost, in pence, of buying r pens and q pencils.
Write down a formula for T in terms of r and q.

8 Rearrange the formula $y = 5x - 20$ to make x the subject.

9 The diagram shows the lengths of the four sides
of a quadrilateral, in terms of x.
P is the length of the perimeter of the quadrilateral.
Write down a formula for P in terms of x.

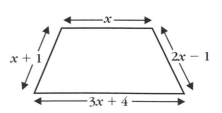

10 Rearrange the formula $t = \dfrac{v}{3} - 4$ to make v the subject.

Now check your answers – see the facing page.

Cover this page while you answer the test questions opposite.

Worked answers

Revise this on...

G   1   Total cost = 15 × 8p = 120p page 62

F   2   Total cost = 8 × £15 + £30 = £120 + £30 = £150 page 62

E   3   T = 2 × 4 + 3 × 5 = 8 + 15 = 23 page 65

E   4   C = n × 8   or   C = 8n page 63

D   5   H = 7 × 2 − 3 × (−3) = 14 + 9 = 23 page 65

D   6   y = 4x − 3 page 65

When y = 7,   7 = 4x − 3

4x = 7 + 3   Add 3 to both sides

4x = 10

x = 10 ÷ 4 = 2.5   Divide both sides by 4

D   7   The cost of r pens is r × 20 or 20r page 63

The cost of q pencils is q × 15 or 15q

Total cost = T = 20r + 15q

D   8   y = 5x − 20 page 64

5x = y + 20   Add 20 to both sides

$x = \dfrac{y + 20}{5}$ Divide both sides by 5

C   9   Perimeter = P = x + (x + 1) + (2x − 1) + (3x + 4) = 7x + 4 pages 62–63

C   10 $t = \dfrac{v}{3} - 4$ page 64

$\dfrac{v}{3} = t + 4$ Add 4 to both sides

v = 3(t + 4)   Multiply both sides by 3

Tick the questions you got right.

Question	1	2	3	4	5	6	7	8	9	10
Grade	G	F	E	E	D	D	D	D	C	C

Mark the grade you are working at on your revision planner on page viii.

Linear equations

- In algebra, letters are used to represent numbers. For example $a = 5$.

- To **solve** an **equation** use the **balancing** method. You must do the same to each side.

$$a + 4 = 7 \quad \rightarrow \quad a + 4 - 4 = 7 - 4 \quad \rightarrow \quad a = 3$$
$$a - 3 = 1 \quad \rightarrow \quad a - 3 + 3 = 1 + 3 \quad \rightarrow \quad a = 4$$
$$5a = 30 \quad \rightarrow \quad 5a \div 5 = 30 \div 5 \quad \rightarrow \quad a = 6$$
$$\frac{a}{2} = 7 \quad \rightarrow \quad \frac{a}{2} \times 2 = 7 \times 2 \quad \rightarrow \quad a = 14$$

- In a combined equation, deal with the $+$ and $-$ first.

$$3a + 7 = 1 \rightarrow 3a + 7 - 7 = 1 - 7 \rightarrow 3a = -6 \rightarrow a = -2$$

Key words

equation	☐
solve	☐
balance	☐

Example — Solve $4x + 3 = 5$

Grade E

Use the balancing method to get the letters on their own on one side.

$$4x + 3 = 5$$
$$4x + 3 - 3 = 5 - 3 \qquad \text{Take 3 from both sides}$$
$$4x = 2$$
$$x = 2 \div 4 \text{ or } \tfrac{2}{4} \qquad \text{Divide both sides by 4}$$

▼

Write the answer as simply as possible.

$$x = \tfrac{1}{2} \text{ or } 0.5$$

WATCH OUT!
Make sure you divide the right way around:
$2 \div 4$ not $4 \div 2$

Example — Solve $\frac{3d}{4} + 5 = 50$

Grade C

Use the balancing method to get the letters on their own on one side.

$$\frac{3d}{4} + 5 = 50$$
$$\frac{3d}{4} = 45 \qquad \text{Take 5 from both sides}$$
$$3d = 180 \qquad \text{Multiply both sides by 4}$$
$$d = 180 \div 3 = 60 \qquad \text{Divide both sides by 3}$$

Example — Solve $6 + 4x = 2x + 16$

Grade D

Use the balancing method to get the letters on their own on one side.

$$6 + 4x = 2x + 16$$
$$6 + 4x - 2x = 2x - 2x + 16 \qquad \text{Take } 2x \text{ from both sides}$$
$$6 + 2x = 16$$
$$6 - 6 + 2x = 16 - 6 \qquad \text{Take 6 from both sides}$$
$$2x = 10$$
$$x = 5 \qquad \text{Divide both sides by 2}$$

- In an equation with **brackets**, **expand** the brackets first.

$$3(x + 1) = 4 \quad \rightarrow \quad 3x + 3 = 4$$

Example

Solve $2(2x - 7) = 7$

$$2(2x - 7) = 7$$

Expand the bracket first. ⟶ $2 \times 2x + 2 \times -7 = 7$

$$4x - 14 = 7$$

WATCH OUT!

Make sure you multiply *every* term inside the bracket. Students often wrongly multiply just the first term, giving $4x - 7$ instead of the correct expansion $4x - 14$.
For more on expanding brackets, see page 44.

Then use the balancing ⟶ $4x - 14 + 14 = 7 + 14$ Add 14 to both sides
method.
$$4x = 21$$
$$x = \frac{21}{4} = 5\frac{1}{4}$$ Divide both sides by 4

Example

Solve $6x + 5 = 2(2x + 1)$

$$6x + 5 = 2(2x + 1)$$

Expand the bracket first. ⟶ $6x + 5 = 4x + 2$

Then use the balancing ⟶ $6x - 4x + 5 = 4x - 4x + 2$ Take 4x from both sides
method.
$$2x + 5 = 2$$
$$2x + 5 - 5 = 2 - 5$$ Take 5 from both sides
$$2x = -3$$
$$x = -\frac{3}{2} = -1\frac{1}{2}$$ Divide both sides by 2

Practice

1 Solve $x + 9 = 0$ **4** Solve $2(5x - 9) = 27$

2 Solve $2x - 7 = 6$ **5** Solve $3(6h - 3) = 4(5h - 4)$

3 Solve $7x - 1 = x - 7$ **6** Solve $\frac{3d}{2} + 4 = 27$

Check your answers on page 168. For full worked solutions see the CD.
See the Student Book on the CD if you need more help.

Question	1	2	3	4	5	6
Grade	F	E	D	D	C	C
Student Book pages	211–214	214–217	219	218	220	215

Solving non-linear equations and inequalities

- A **quadratic** equation has an x^2 term (and no higher power of x).

- Quadratic equations can have 0, 1 or 2 solutions.

Key words

square ☐   quadratic ☐

square root ☐

Example Solve $4x^2 - 7 = 93$

Grade C

Use the balancing method to get the x^2 term on its own.

$$4x^2 - 7 = 93$$
$$4x^2 - 7 + 7 = 93 + 7 \quad \text{Add 7 to both sides}$$
$$4x^2 = 100$$
$$x^2 = 25 \quad \text{Divide both sides by 4}$$

Find the **square root**.

$$x = \pm 5, \ x = 5 \text{ or } x = -5$$

- You can find approximate solutions of more complicated equations by **trial and improvement**.

- A **cubic** equation has an x^3 term (and no higher power of x).

Key words

cube ☐   cubic ☐

trial and improvement ☐

Example The equation $2x^3 + 3x = 400$ has a solution between 5 and 6. Use a trial and improvement method to find this solution. Give your answer correct to one decimal place.

Grade C

Work out $2x^3 + 3x$ using different values of x, until you get near to 400. Start with the x values given.

When x = 5, $2x^3 + 3x = 265$ Smaller than 400
When x = 6, $2x^3 + 3x = 450$ Bigger than 400
When x = 5.5, $2x^3 + 3x = 349.25$ Smaller than 400
When x = 5.7, $2x^3 + 3x = 387.486$ Smaller than 400
When x = 5.8, $2x^3 + 3x = 407.624$ Bigger than 400

TIP

Work out carefully:
$(2 \times 5 \times 5 \times 5) + (3 \times 5) = 265$

EXAMINER'S TIP

Always write down an accurate answer, with decimals if possible.

So x lies between 5.7 and 5.8. Try the half-way value.

When x = 5.75, $2x^3 + 3x = 397.468$ Smaller than 400

The solution is between x = 5.75 and x = 5.8
Any number in this range rounds to 5.8 (to 1 d.p.).
So x = 5.8 (to 1 d.p.)

EXAMINER'S TIP

Remember to write down the solution to the equation. This is the value of x (5.8), not the number calculated (397.468).

- An **inequality** is a statement with one of these signs.

  $>$ means **greater than** $\geq$ means **greater than or equal to**
  $<$ means **less than** $\leq$ means **less than or equal to**

Key words

inequality ☐   integer ☐

- You can solve inequalities using the balancing method.

Example

Write down the integer values of x that satisfy the inequality $-2 \leq x < 3$

Grade C

Draw a number line of the inequality to help.

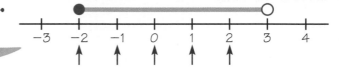

WATCH OUT!

Do not confuse $<$ and $\leq$. Notice the 'equals sign' at the bottom of the $\leq$ sign.

The empty circle shows that 3 **is not** included in the inequality and the solid circle shows that -2 **is** included.
The numbers shown by arrows are the integer values of x.

The integer values of x are $-2, -1, 0, 1, 2$.

Example

Solve $2x + 3 < 7$

Grade C

Use the balancing method to make x the subject, just like an equation.

$$2x + 3 < 7$$
$$2x + 3 - 3 < 7 - 3 \quad \text{Take 3 from both sides}$$
$$2x < 4$$
$$x < 2 \quad \text{Divide both sides by 2}$$

Practice

Grade C

1 Solve $2x^2 + 2 = 100$

Grade C

2 The equation $4x^3 - x^2 = 50$ has a solution between 2 and 3. Use a trial and improvement method to find this solution. Give your answer to one decimal place.

3 Draw a number line to show the inequality $2 \leq x < 6$

Grade C

4 Write down the integer values of x that satisfy the inequality $-1 < x \leq 5$

Grade C

5 Solve $3x - 5 > 4$

Grade C

Check your answers on page 168. For full worked solutions see the CD.
See the Student Book on the CD if you need more help.

Question	1	2	3	4	5
Grade	C	C	C	C	C
Student Book pages	542	542–543	407–408	406	406

Solving equations and inequalities: topic test

Check how well you know this topic by answering these questions.
First cover the answers on the facing page.

Test questions

1   Solve

$$x + 3 = 7$$

2   Solve

$$4x - 3 = 21$$

3   Solve

$$5x + 2 = -4 + 3x$$

4   Solve

$$7x + 13 = 3(x + 5)$$

5   Solve

$$\frac{x}{3} + 2 = 1$$

6   Use a trial and improvement method to find a solution to

$$3x^3 + x^2 = 53$$

Give your answer correct to one decimal place.

7   **(a)** Write down the inequality that is shown on this number line:

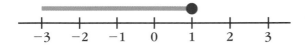

(b) Copy the number line below and show the inequality $-2 < x \leqslant 3$

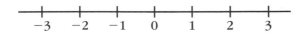

8   Write down the integer values of x that satisfy the inequality

$$-3 < x \leqslant 2$$

Now check your answers – see the facing page.

Cover this page while you answer the test questions opposite.

Worked answers

Revise this on...

F   **1**

$$x + 3 = 7$$
$$x + 3 - 3 = 7 - 3 \qquad \text{Subtract 3 from both sides}$$
$$x = 4$$

page 68

E   **2**

$$4x - 3 = 21$$
$$4x = 24 \qquad \text{Add 3 to both sides}$$
$$x = 6 \qquad \text{Divide both sides by 4}$$

page 68

D   **3**

$$5x + 2 = -4 + 3x$$
$$2x + 2 = -4 \qquad \text{Subtract 3x from both sides}$$
$$2x = -6 \qquad \text{Subtract 2 from both sides}$$
$$x = -3 \qquad \text{Divide both sides by 2}$$

page 68

C   **4**

$$7x + 13 = 3(x + 5)$$
$$7x + 13 = 3x + 15 \qquad \text{Expand the bracket}$$
$$4x + 13 = 15 \qquad \text{Subtract 3x from both sides}$$
$$4x = 2 \qquad \text{Subtract 13 from both sides}$$
$$x = \frac{2}{4} = \frac{1}{2} \qquad \text{Divide both sides by 4}$$

page 69

C   **5**

$$\frac{x}{3} + 2 = 1$$

$$\frac{x}{3} = -1 \qquad \text{Subtract 2 from both sides}$$

$$x = -3 \qquad \text{Multiply both sides by 3}$$

page 68

C   **6**

When $x = 1$, $3x^3 + x^2 = 4$ Smaller than 53
When $x = 2$, $3x^3 + x^2 = 28$ Smaller than 53
When $x = 3$, $3x^3 + x^2 = 90$ Bigger than 53
When $x = 2.5$, $3x^3 + x^2 = 53.125$ Bigger than 53
When $x = 2.4$, $3x^3 + x^2 = 47.232$ Smaller than 53
When $x = 2.45$, $3x^3 + x^2 = 50.120\ 875$ Smaller than 53
The solution is between 2.45 and 2.5. Any number in this range rounds to 2.5 (to 1 d.p.).
So $x = 2.5$ (to 1 d.p.)

page 70

C   **7**   (a) $x \leqslant 1$

page 71

(b)

C   **8** $-3 < x$ means the numbers are greater than -3 (not including -3).
$x \leqslant 2$ means the numbers are less than or equal to 2.
So the integer values are $-2, -1, 0, 1, 2$.

page 71

Tick the questions you got right.

Question	1	2	3	4	5	6	7	8
Grade	F	E	D	C	C	C	C	C

Mark the grade you are working at on your revision planner on page viii.

Algebra: subject test

Exam practice questions

1   Simplify $k + 3k - 2k$

2   Simplify $4g + 7h - 2g + 5h$

3   Simplify $q \times q \times q$

4   Simplify $y^2 + y^2 + y^2 + y^2$

5   Expand $3(a - 2b)$

6   Expand and simplify $4(c - 2d) + 2(c + 3d)$

7   Expand $x(2x - 3y)$

8   Factorise $3w - 12$

9   Factorise $x^2 - 5x$

10   This is a series of diagrams made from dots.

Diagram 1   Diagram 2   Diagram 3

(a)   Draw Diagram 4.

(b)   Complete the table.

Diagram	1	2	3	4	5
Number of dots	4	7	10		

(c)   Find the general rule, in terms of n, for the number of dots in the nth diagram.

11   These five numbers are part of a number sequence: 8, 11, 14, 17, 20

Write down the general rule, in terms of n, for the nth term in the sequence.

12   This is part of the travel graph for a motorist.

(a)   How far from home is the motorist at 4 pm?

(b)   For how long was the motorist stationary?

(c)   What was the average speed, in km/h, of the motorist after 3 pm?

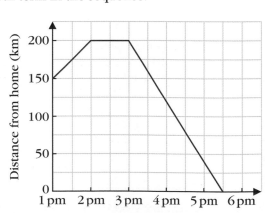

13 (a) Complete the table of values for $y = 3x - 1$.

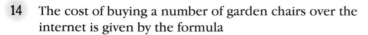

x	-2	-1	0	1	2	3
y						

   (b) On a copy of the grid, draw the graph of $y = 3x - 1$.

   (c) Use your graph to find the value of x when $y = -2.5$

14 The cost of buying a number of garden chairs over the
    internet is given by the formula

    total cost = number of chairs × £8.50 + delivery charge

    Work out the total cost for 6 chairs, with a delivery
    charge of £15.

15 At a shop, CDs cost £3 and DVDs cost £5.
    T is the total cost, in £, of buying c CDs and d DVDs.
    Write down a formula for T in terms of c and d.

16 (a) Write down an expression, in terms of x, for the total of
        the angles in the triangle.

   (b) Write down an equation in terms of x.

   (c) Solve your equation to find the value of x.

17 Solve $x + 4 = 9$

18 Solve $2x - 3 = 15$

19 Solve $3(x + 2) = 24$

20 Solve $4x - 1 = 2(x + 3)$

21 $-3 \leqslant n < 4$, where n is an integer.
    Write down all the possible values of n.

22 The equation $3x^3 - x^2 = 58$ has a solution between 2 and 3.
    Use a trial and improvement method to find this solution.
    Give your answer correct to one decimal place.

Check your answers on page 168. For full worked solutions see the CD.

Tick the questions you got right.

Question	1	2	3	4	5	6	7	8	9	10ab	10c	11	12ab	12c	13	14	15	16	17	18	19	20	21	22
Grade	G	E	D	E	D	C	C	C	C	F	C	C	E	D	E	E	E	D	F	E	D	C	C	C
Revise this on page	42	42	42	42	44	44	44	45	45	48–49	48		54		56	62	63	62	68	68	69	69	71	70

Mark the grade you are working at on your revision planner on page viii.

Go to the pages shown to revise for the ones you got wrong.

Algebra

Manipulative algebra

- An **algebraic expression** is a collection of letters, symbols and numbers:

    $a + 3b - 2c$

- You can combine **like terms** by adding and subtracting them:

    $2a + 3a = 5a$ and $3b + 4b - b = 6b$

- You can simplify algebraic expressions by collecting like terms together:

    $2a - 4b + 3a + 5b$ simplifies to $5a + b$

- **Expanding** the brackets means multiplying to remove the brackets:

    $4(3a + b) = 12a + 4b$

- **Factorising** means splitting up an expression using brackets:

    $12a + 4b = 4(3a + b)$

Patterns and sequences

- In a number pattern or **sequence** there is always a **rule** to get from one number to the next.

- To find the rule for the nth term of a number pattern, use a table of values.

Term number	1	2	3	4
Term	5	8	11	14
Difference		+3 +3 +3		

The rule is $3n + 2$.

Coordinates and graphs

- The number line is **1-dimensional** or **1-D**. You can describe positions on the number line using one number or coordinate, for example (2).

- Flat shapes are **2-dimensional** or **2-D**. You can describe positions on a flat shape using two numbers or coordinates, for example (2, 1).

- Solid shapes are **3-dimensional** or **3-D**. You can describe positions in a solid shape using three numbers or coordinates, for example (4, 1, 2).

- A graph representing a **linear relationship** is always a straight line.

- **Distance–time graphs** are used to relate the distance travelled to the time taken, and to calculate speeds.

- The **equation of a line** uses algebra to show a relationship between the x- and y-coordinates of points on the line.

- An equation containing an x-term and no higher powers of x (such as x^2) is a **linear equation**.

- The graph of a linear equation is a straight line.

- An equation containing an x^2-term is called a **quadratic equation**.

- The graph of a quadratic equation is a curved quadratic graph, or parabola. It has a symmetrical U-shape: $\cup$ or $\cap$.

Formulae

- A **word formula** uses words to represent a relationship between quantities. For example:

  pay = rate of pay $\times$ hours worked

- An **algebraic formula** uses letters to represent a relationship between quantities. For example, the perimeter of a rectangle, P, is related to its length l and width w by

  $P = 2l + 2w$

- The **subject** of a formula appears on its own on one side of the formula and does not appear on the other side. For example:

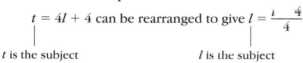

  $t = 4l + 4$ can be rearranged to give $l = \dfrac{t - 4}{4}$

  t is the subject l is the subject

Solving equations and inequalities

- In algebra, letters are used to represent numbers. For example $a = 5$.

- To keep an **equation** balanced you must do the same to each side.

  $a + 4 = 7 \quad \rightarrow \quad a + 4 - 4 = 7 - 4 \quad \rightarrow \quad a = 3$

  $a - 3 = 1 \quad \rightarrow \quad a - 3 + 3 = 1 + 3 \quad \rightarrow \quad a = 4$

  $5a = 30 \quad \rightarrow \quad 5a \div 5 = 30 \div 5 \quad \rightarrow \quad a = 6$

  $\dfrac{a}{2} = 7 \quad \rightarrow \quad \dfrac{a}{2} \times 2 = 7 \times 2 \quad \rightarrow \quad a = 14$

- In a combined equation, deal with the $+$ and $-$ first.

  $3a + 7 = 1 \rightarrow 3a + 7 - 7 = 1 - 7 \rightarrow 3a = -6 \rightarrow a = -2$

- In an equation with **brackets**, **expand** the brackets first.

  $3(x + 1) = 4 \quad \rightarrow \quad 3x + 3 = 4$

- Quadratic equations can have 0, 1 or 2 solutions.

- You can find approximate solutions of more complicated equations by **trial and improvement**.

- $>$ means **greater than**
  $<$ means **less than**
  $\geq$ means **greater than or equal to**
  $\leq$ means **less than or equal to**

Naming and calculating angles

- An **acute angle** is less than 90°.

- An **obtuse angle** is between 90° and 180°.

- A **reflex angle** is between 180° and 360°.

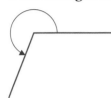

- The angles on a straight line add up to 180°.

- The angles at a point add up to 360°.

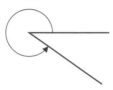

- Where two straight lines cross, the opposite angles are equal. They are called **vertically opposite angles**.

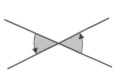

- The angles in a triangle add up to 180°.

- The angles in a quadrilateral add up to 360°.

- An **isosceles triangle** has two equal angles and two equal sides.

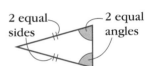

2 equal sides　2 equal angles

- An **equilateral triangle** has three 60° angles and three equal sides.

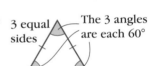

3 equal sides　The 3 angles are each 60°

Example

ABCD is a straight line.
Find angle *PQC*.

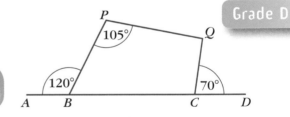

TIP

This is angle PQC.

Identify the angle you need to find. ———•

Use the angles given to work out other angles inside the quadrilateral. Give a reason.

Use these three angles of the quadrilateral to work out the fourth one.

Angle PBC = 180 − 120 = 60°
(angles on a straight line)

Angle QCB = 180 − 70 = 110°
(angles on a straight line)

Angle PQC = 360 − 60 − 110 − 105 = 85°
(angles in a quadrilateral add up to 360°)

WATCH OUT!

A *reason* is 'why'.
A common error is to say 'how' instead of 'why'.

EXAMINER'S TIP

Always ask yourself if the answer is sensible. Diagrams are not accurately drawn, but you can usually tell whether an angle is acute or obtuse.

Example

$AB = AC = AD$
Angle $BAC = 36°$
Angle $ADC = 40°$
Find angle BCD.

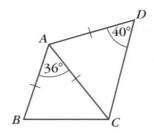

Identify the angle you need to find. ———————•

▼

Identify what the diagram tells you. Here, triangles ACD and ABC are isosceles.

Angle ACD = angle ADC = 40°

Angle ABC = angle ACB = $(180 − 36) ÷ 2$
      (angles in a triangle)
          = $144 ÷ 2 = 72°$

Angle BCD = angle ACB + angle ACD = $72 + 40 = 112°$

Practice

3

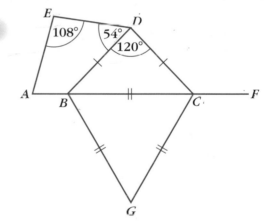

Grade E

1 Work out the value of x.
Give a reason for your answer.

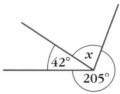

Grade D

2 AB and CD are straight lines.
Work out the values of w, x and y.
Give reasons for your answers.

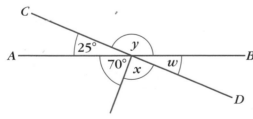

$ABCF$ is a straight line.
BCG is an equilateral triangle.
$DB = DC$
$BC = CG = BG$
Find (a) angle DCF **Grade D**

     (b) angle EAB **Grade C**

     (c) angle DCG.   **Grade D**

Give reasons for your answers.

Check your answers on page 169. For full worked solutions see the CD.
See the Student Book on the CD if you need more help.

Question	1	2	3a	3b	3c
Grade	E	D	D	C	D
Student Book pages	104–105	103–105	104–107	104–105	125

Working with angles

- **Parallel lines** are shown with arrowheads.

- **Alternate angles** are equal.

- **Corresponding angles** are equal.

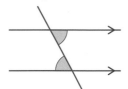 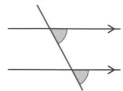

Key words

parallel lines ☐
alternate angles ☐
corresponding angles ☐

Example

ABCD and *DEFG* are straight lines.
RS is parallel to *PQ*.
CE = DE
Find the value of *x*.

EXAMINER'S TIP

If you are told that the diagram is not accurately drawn do not measure the angles with a protractor, you need to work them out.

Diagram NOT accurately drawn

Find angles that are the same as the given one (*ABR* here).

Angle CBF = 35°
  (vertically opposite to angle ABR)

Angle DCE = 35°
  (corresponding angle to angle CBF)

Angle CDE = 35°
  (base angles of an isosceles triangle)

Now work towards *x*. ———

Angle CED = $180 - 35 - 35 = 110°$
  (angles in a triangle)

Angle CEF = $180 - 110 = 70°$
  (angles on a straight line)

Angle EFS = $x = 70°$
  (alternate angles)

TIP

If you cannot see the way to the answer, write onto the diagram any angles you can find.

TIP

Although diagrams are 'NOT accurately drawn', you can usually tell if angles
- are equal
- are unrelated
- add up to 180°
- add up to 360°.

Grade C

Example

PQRS is a straight line.
AB is parallel to *CD*.
RS = RD
Angle *PQB* = 56°
Show that angle *RDS* is 28°.

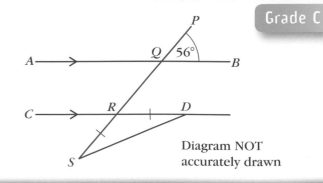

Diagram NOT accurately drawn

Grade C

Find angles that are the same as the given one. ——→ Angle QRD = 56°
(corresponding angle to angle PQB)

▼

Now work into triangle *SRD*. ——→ Angle SRD = 180 − 56 = 124°
(angles on a straight line)

▼

The final step. ——————→ Angle RSD = angle RDS = x
(base angles of an isosceles triangle)
x + x + 124 = 180
(angles in a triangle)
So 2x = 56° and x = angle RDS = 28°

TIP

'Show that' questions are the same as 'Work out' or 'Find' questions except that
• the answer is given
• you *must* give all the stages of the working out *and* give reasons.

Practice

Grade D   **1**   *AB* is parallel to *CD*.
PQ is parallel to *RS*.
Angle *APQ* = 47°

Find the size of the angles marked *a* to *d*.
Give reasons for your answers.

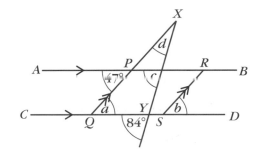

Grade D   **2**   *AB* = *BE*
BE is parallel to *CF*.
Angle *AEB* = 35°

Find   (a) angle *EFC*
        (b) angle *CBE*
        (c) angle *DCF*.
Give reasons for your answers.

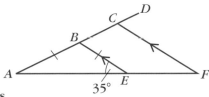

Grade C   **3**   *AB* = *AC*
CB = *CD*
AB is parallel to *CD*.
Angle *ACB* = 34°
Show that angle *CDB* = 73°.

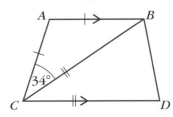

4   *PX* = *PQ*
XQ is parallel to *RY*.
Show that triangle *PRY* is isosceles.   **Grade C**

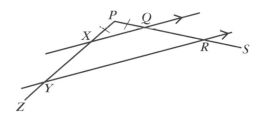

Check your answers on page 169. For full worked solutions see the CD.
See the Student Book on the CD if you need more help.

Question	1	2	3	4
Grade	D	D	C	C
Student Book pages	109–113	109–113	113–114	113–114

Angles: topic test

Check how well you know this topic by answering these questions.
First cover the answers on the facing page.

Test questions

1 Write down the mathematical name for these types of angles:

(a)

(b)

2 (a) (i) Find the value of a.

(ii) Give a reason for your answer.

(b) Find the value of b.

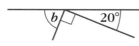

3 (a) Work out the size of angle ABC.

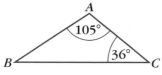

(b) Give a reason for your answer.

4 (a) Find the value of c.

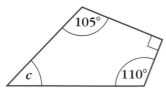

(b) Give a reason for your answer.

5 Triangle DEF is isosceles.
$DE = DF$
Angle $EDF = 80°$
Work out the size of angle DEF.

Now check your answers – see the facing page.

82

6 (a) Find the value of d.

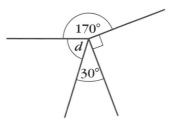

(b) Give a reason for your answer.

7 Triangle KLM is isosceles.
LMN is a straight line.
$KL = KM$
Angle $KMN = 116°$

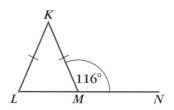

Work out (a) angle KLM (b) angle LKM.

8 Find the values of x, y and z.
Give reasons for your answers.

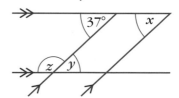

9

(a) Find the value of x.
Give a reason for your answer.

(b) Show that $y = 52°$.

Cover this page while you answer the test questions opposite.

Worked answers

Revise this on...

G 1 (a) Right angle (b) Reflex angle — page 78

F 2 (a) (i) $a = 180 - 115 = 65°$ — page 78
(ii) Angles on a straight line add up to 180°.

(b) $b = 180 - 90 - 20 = 70°$

F 3 (a) Angle ABC $= 180 - 105 - 36 = 39°$ — page 78

(b) Angles in a triangle add up to 180°.

E 4 (a) $c = 360 - 110 - 105 - 90 = 55°$ — page 78

(b) Angles in a quadrilateral add up to 360°.

E 5 Triangle DEF is isosceles so angle DEF = angle DFE — page 78
Angle DEF $= \frac{1}{2}(180 - 80) = 50°$

E 6 (a) $d = 360 - 30 - 170 - 90 = 70°$ — page 78

(b) Angles at a point add up to 360°.

D 7 (a) Angle KLM = angle KML $= 180 - 116 = 64°$ — page 78

(b) Angle LKM $= 180 - 2 \times 64 = 180 - 128 = 52°$

D 8 $x = 37°$ (corresponding angles) — page 80
$y = 37°$ (alternate angles)
$z = 180 - 37 = 143°$ (angles on a straight line)

E 9 (a) $x = 360 - 286 = 74°$ (angles at a point) — page 78

C (b) Angle alongside 126° $= 180 - 126 = 54°$ (angles on a straight line)
Third angle in the triangle $= 180 - 74 - 54 = 52°$
$y = 52°$ (vertically opposite angles)

Tick the questions you got right.

Question	1	2	3	4	5	6	7	8	9a	9b
Grade	G	F	F	E	E	E	D	D	E	C

Mark the grade you are working at on your revision planner on page ix.

Polygons

- In a **regular polygon** all sides are equal and all angles are equal.

- The sum of the **interior angles** of a polygon with n sides is $(n \times 180°) - 360°$, usually written $(n - 2) \times 180°$

- The sum of the **exterior angles** of any polygon is 360°.

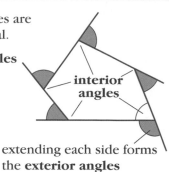

interior angles

extending each side forms the **exterior angles**

Key words

polygon ☐	octagon (8) ☐
regular polygon ☐	decagon (10) ☐
pentagon (5) ☐	interior angle ☐
hexagon (6) ☐	exterior angle ☐

Example

A regular polygon has an interior angle of 156°.
(a) Work out how many sides it has.
(b) Find the sum of the interior angles of this polygon.

Grade D

Find the exterior angle. ⟶ (a)

156° ⟍exterior angle

▼

Work out how many of these there are in 360°.

Exterior angle = 180 − 156 = 24°
  (angles on a straight line)
360 ÷ 24 = 15
The polygon has 15 sides.

TIP
It is easier to work with exterior angles because these always add up to 360°.

Use $(n - 2) \times 180°$ ⟶ (b) $n = 15$
$(n - 2) \times 180° = (15 - 2) \times 180°$
$= 13 \times 180°$
$= 2340°$

- A pattern of shapes which fit together without leaving gaps or overlapping is called a **tessellation**.

- Shapes which are exactly the same size and shape are **congruent**.

These shapes are congruent

Key words

tessellation ☐
congruent ☐

Example

Show how this shape will tessellate.
You must draw at least six shapes.

Grade E

Fit sides that are the same ⟶
length together.

TIP
Only consider the shape as it is given and the shape after a half turn (upside down).

▼

Show the pattern continuing ⟶
in both directions.

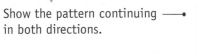

TIP
Keep the pattern as simple as possible.

Practice

1 Write down the letters of the shapes that are congruent.

Grade F

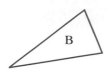 A

B

 C

 D

2 Show how these shapes will tessellate.

Grade F

(a)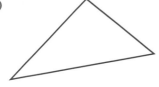

(b)

3 Find the size of the angles marked *a* and *b*.

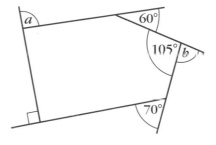

Grade E

4 *QRST* is a square.
PQT is an equilateral triangle.
(a) Show that angle *PTS* is 150°.
(b) Work out the size of angle *PST*.
(c) Show that angle *PXQ* is 75°.

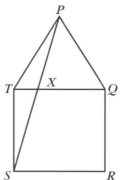

Grade D

5 *ABCD* is part of a regular octagon.
DCE is part of a regular hexagon.
(a) Work out the size of angle *BCE*.
(b) Explain why angle *CBE* = angle *CEB*.

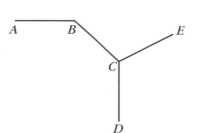

Grade C

Check your answers on page 169. For full worked solutions see the CD.
See the Student Book on the CD if you need more help.

Question	1	2	3	4	5
Grade	F	F	E	D	C
Student Book pages	131–132	133–134	115–118	115–118	115–118

Drawing and calculating

- A **bearing** is the angle measured from facing North and turning clockwise. It is always a three-figure number.

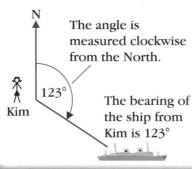

N

The angle is measured clockwise from the North.

123°

Kim

The bearing of the ship from Kim is 123°

- The **locus** of points equidistant from **one point** is a circle.

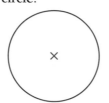

×

- The locus of points equidistant from **two lines** is made by bisecting the angle formed where they meet.

Key words

locus ☐   angle bisector ☐
perpendicular bisector ☐

- The locus of points equidistant from **two points** is the **perpendicular bisector** of the line joining the two points.

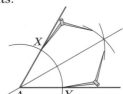
×   ×

X

A   Y

Example

Great Yarmouth is 30 kilometres from Norwich on a bearing of 095°.
Wells-next-the-Sea is 45 kilometres from Norwich on a bearing of 320°.

Grade D

(a) Draw an accurate scale diagram using a scale of 1 cm for 5 kilometres.

Grade C

(b) Radio X, based at Norwich, has a range of 20 kilometres.
Shade the area that can receive broadcasts from Radio X.

Grade C

(c) An aircraft flies on a path equidistant from Norwich and Wells-next-the-Sea.
Construct this flight path on your diagram.

Use the scale to work out the ⟶ lengths for the diagrams.

▼

Mark North and your starting town.

▼

Use a protractor to measure the bearing. Draw accurate lengths using a ruler.

▼

Locus of points 20 km from Norwich is a circle, radius 20 km.

The flight path is the perpendicular bisector of the line joining Norwich to Wells-next-the-Sea.

TIP

Draw the perpendicular bisector:

A   B

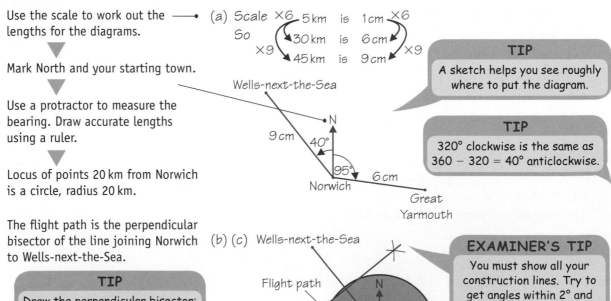

(a) Scale ×6 ⟍ 5 km   is   1 cm ×6
So   30 km   is   6 cm
×9 ⟍ 45 km   is   9 cm ×9

TIP

A sketch helps you see roughly where to put the diagram.

Wells-next-the-Sea

N

9 cm   40°

95°   6 cm

Norwich

Great Yarmouth

TIP

320° clockwise is the same as 360 − 320 = 40° anticlockwise.

(b) (c) Wells-next-the-Sea

Flight path   N

Norwich   4 cm

Great Yarmouth

EXAMINER'S TIP

You must show all your construction lines. Try to get angles within 2° and lengths within 1 mm.

- **Pythagoras' theorem** states that in a right-angled triangle the square on the **hypotenuse** is equal to the sum of the squares on the other two sides.

$$c^2 = a^2 + b^2 \quad \text{or} \quad a^2 + b^2 = c^2$$

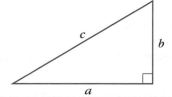

Key words

Pythagoras' theorem ☐
hypotenuse ☐

Example

Find the length of *AB*.

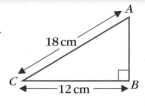

Grade C

TIP
The hypotenuse is the longest side = 18 cm

Use Pythagoras' theorem. ────▸ $18^2 = 12^2 + AB^2$

WATCH OUT!
Don't forget to take the square root.

Rearrange to make the ────▸ $AB^2 = 18^2 - 12^2 = 180$
unknown side the subject.

$AB = \sqrt{180} = 13.4\,cm$

TIP
Always check that your answer leaves the hypotenuse as the longest side.

TIP
For more on rearranging formulae see page 64.

Practice

1 (a) Use a ruler and protractor to make an accurate scale drawing of the diagram shown.
Use a scale of 1 cm = 5 km.

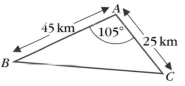

Grade D

Grade C (b) Shade all points that are 20 km or less from *C*.

Grade C (c) Construct the locus of points that are the same distance from *AB* as from *AC*.

2 Charlbury is 9 kilometres North of Witney.
Woodstock is 11 kilometres from Witney on a bearing of 055°.
Draw an accurate scale diagram using a scale of 1 cm to 2 km.
Use your drawing to find the distance and bearing of Woodstock from Charlbury.

Grade C

3 Construct a triangle with sides 7 cm, 8 cm and 9 cm.
Bisect the angle between the sides of length 8 cm and 9 cm.
Construct the perpendicular bisector of the side of length 7 cm.
Measure the obtuse angle where your bisector and perpendicular bisector intersect.

Grade C

4 Work out the length of the side marked with a letter in each triangle.

Grade C

(a)

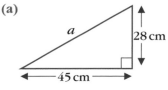

(b)

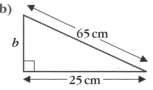

(c)

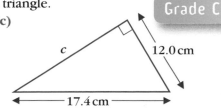

Check your answers on pages 169–170. For full worked solutions see the CD.
See the Student Book on the CD if you need more help.

Question	1a	1bc	2	3	4
Grade	D	C	C	C	C
Student Book pages	134–137	141–146	138–141	142–143	466–472

2-D shapes: topic test

Check how well you know this topic by answering these questions.
First cover the answers on the facing page.

Test questions

1 Write the mathematical name for each of these shapes.

(a)   **(b)** 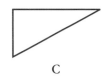   **(c)**   **(d)**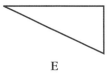

2 Work out the sum of the interior angles of an irregular pentagon.

3 Write down the letters of the shape(s) that are congruent to shape A.

A   B   C   D   E

4 The exterior angle of a regular polygon is 15°. Work out how many sides this polygon has.

5 The bearing of *B* from *A* is 056°. Write down the bearing of *A* from *B*.

6 Mark two points, *A* and *B*, and construct the locus of the points that are equidistant from *A* and *B*.

7 Draw an angle of about 50°. Construct the bisector of this angle.

8 *A*, *B* and *C* are three towns.
The bearing of *B* from *A* is 070° and the distance is 50 km.
The bearing of *C* from *B* is 130° and the distance is 60 km.
Use a scale of 1 cm = 10 km to draw a scale diagram.
Use your diagram to find the distance and bearing of *A* from *C*.

9 Work out the length of **(a)** *AD*   **(b)** *AC*.

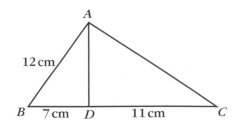

Now check your answers – see the facing page.

Cover this page while you answer the test questions opposite.

Worked answers

Revise this on...

G 1 (a) Kite (b) Hexagon (c) Parallelogram (d) Trapezium –

F 2 Angle sum = $(n - 2) \times 180°$ page 84
$n = 5$ so angle sum = $3 \times 180° = 540°$

F 3 Shape C page 84

D 4 Sum of the exterior angles is 360°. page 84
Number of sides = $360 \div 15 = 24$

D 5 $056 + 180 = 236°$ (The bearing is in the opposite direction so page 86
a half turn of $\pm180°$ is used.)

D 6 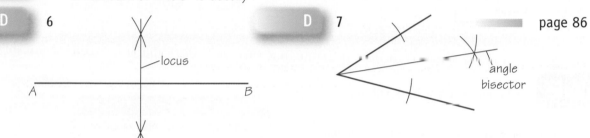 **D** 7 page 86

D 8 page 86

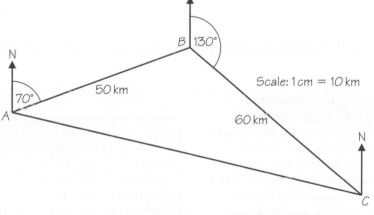

The bearing of A from C is 283° and the distance is 95 km.

C 9 (a) $AD^2 + 7^2 = 12^2$ so $AD^2 = 12^2 - 7^2 = 95$, $AD = \sqrt{95} = 9.75$ cm page 87

(b) $AC^2 = AD^2 + CD^2 = 95 + 11^2 = 216$ so $AC = \sqrt{216} = 14.7$ cm

Tick the questions you got right.

Question	1	2	3	4	5	6	7	8	9
Grade	G	F	F	D	D	D	D	D	C

Mark the grade you are working at on your revision planner on page ix.

Units of measurement

- Approximate **conversions** between units:

Metric	Imperial
8 km	5 miles
1 kg	2.2 pounds
25 g	1 ounce
1 l	$1\frac{3}{4}$ pints
4.5 l	1 gallon
1 m	39 inches
30 cm	1 foot
2.5 cm	1 inch

- **Speed** $= \dfrac{\text{distance}}{\text{time}}$

- **Average speed** $= \dfrac{\text{total distance}}{\text{total time}}$

- Units of speed are miles per hour (mph), kilometres per hour (km/h) and metres per second (m/s).

- If you make a measurement correct to a given unit the true value lies in a range that extends half a unit below and half a unit above the measurement.

Key words

- metric ☐
- imperial ☐
- conversion ☐
- speed ☐
- average speed ☐
- timetable ☐

Example   Change 50 litres into gallons.

Grade E

Use the unitary method. ——→ 4.5 l is 1 gallon

1 l is $\dfrac{1}{4.5}$ gallons

50 l is $50 \times \dfrac{1}{4.5} = 11.1$ gallons.

TIP
Gallons are larger than litres so there are less of them. So you *divide* by 4.5 to turn litres into gallons.

Example   Here is part of a railway **timetable**.

Grade F

(a) How long does it take the 08 27 train from Lincoln to get to Sheffield?

(b) How long does the last train take to travel from Retford to Worksop?

(c) Gillian lives in Retford. She has to be in Sheffield by quarter to eleven. What is the time of the latest train she can catch?

	First train			*Last train*
Lincoln	07 04	08 27	09 27	17 16
Retford	07 40	09 03	10 03	17 52
Worksop	07 54	09 15	10 15	18 04
Shireoaks	07 57	09 18	—	—
Sheffield	08 26	09 47	10 46	18 26

Find the column for the 08 27 train. Go down to the Sheffield row.

(a) The 08 27 gets to Sheffield at 09 47
09 47 − 08 27 = 1 hour 20 minutes

WATCH OUT!
A common error is to use a calculator in its decimal mode.

Use the times in the last column.

(b) The last train leaves Retford at 17 52 and arrives in Worksop at 18 04. This is 8 minutes before 18 00 and 4 minutes after. It takes 12 minutes.

TIP
It is best to work 'in pieces' here and add them up.

(c) Quarter to eleven is 10 45 so the third train is too late. She must be at the station before 09 03 to catch the second train.

Example

Bianca cycles 3600 metres in 12 minutes.
Work out her average speed in kilometres per hour (km/h).

Change to the units you want. ⟶ 12 minutes $= \frac{12}{60} = \frac{1}{5}$ hour

3600 metres = 3.6 kilometres

TIP
The speed is in km/h, so work in hours. (If the speed is in m/s, work in seconds.)

WATCH OUT!
12 minutes is not 0.12 hour.

Speed $= \dfrac{\text{distance}}{\text{time}}$

$= \dfrac{3.6\,\text{km}}{\frac{1}{5}\,\text{hour}} = 3.6 \times 5 = 18$ km/h

Practice

1 Use the railway timetable in the example on page 90 to answer these questions.

   (a) At what time does the second train get to Worksop?

   (b) How long does the last train take to get from Retford to Sheffield?

   (c) Ravi takes 15 minutes to walk from home to the Lincoln station.
       He allows 5 minutes to buy a ticket and get on to the platform.
       What is the latest time he can leave home to catch the first train?

2 Write down the readings on these scales.

   (a)  **Grade G**   (b) 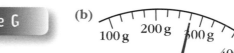   **Grade F**

3 Change

   (a) 8 kg into pounds   (b) 65 miles into kilometres   (c) 75 cm into inches.

4 Asif runs 30 km in $2\frac{1}{2}$ hours. Work out his average speed.

5 A car is travelling at 42 km/h. Work out how far it travels in

   (a) 3 hours   (b) 1 hour 20 minutes   (c) 10 minutes.

6 A plane is flying at 720 km/h. Work out how many metres it flies in 5 seconds.

Check your answers on page 170. For full worked solutions see the CD.
See the Student Book on the CD if you need more help.

Question	1ab	1c	2a	2b	3	4	5	6
Grade	G	F	G	F	E	D	C	C
Student Book pages	272–274		188–190		266–267	363–364	363–364	363–364

Measure: topic test

Check how well you know this topic by answering these questions.
First cover the answers on the facing page.

Test questions

1 Which is the most sensible metric unit for measuring

    (a) the length of a pencil   **(b)** the weight of an exercise book

    (c) the capacity of a cup?

2 Write

    (a) 5.6 kilograms in grams   **(b)** 2360 centimetres in metres   **(c)** 750 ml in litres.

3 Change these to 24-hour clock times.

    (a) 3:25 am   **(b)** 10:50 am   **(c)** 2:35 pm   **(d)** quarter to eleven in the evening

4 Change these to 12-hour clock times (am or pm).

    (a) 07:45   **(b)** 10:30   **(c)** 17:25   **(d)** 22:40   **(e)** 12:05

5 For each scale write down what one small division is worth and write down the measurement shown by the arrow.

    (a)
    (b)

    (c)
    (d)

6 A film starts at 18:40 and finishes at 21:15.
Work out the running time in hours and minutes.

7 14 pounds = 1 stone
William weighs 8 stone 3 pounds.
Work out William's weight in kilograms.

8 Alan runs 20 km in 1 hour 40 minutes.
Work out his average speed in km/h.

9 Pia drives the 95 kilometres from London to Brighton at an average speed of 42 km/h.
How long does she take?

Now check your answers – see the facing page.

Cover this page while you answer the test questions opposite.

Worked answers

Revise this on...

G   1   (a) centimetres   (b) grams   (c) millilitres   page 90

G   2   (a) 5600 g   (b) 23.6 m   (c) 0.75 l   page 90

G   3   (a) 03:25   (b) 10:50   (c) 14:35   (d) 22:45   page 90

G   4   (a) 7:45 am   (b) 10:30 am   (c) 5:25 pm   page 90
       (d) 10:40 pm   (e) 12:05 pm

G   5   (a) 0.1, 1.3   (b) 25 g, 175 g   page 90

F   (c) 6 minutes, 10:42   (d) 20, 360

E   6   From 18 40 to 19 00 is 20 minutes   page 90
      From 19 00 to 21 00 is 2 hours
      From 21 00 to 21 15 is 15 minutes
      Total running time — 2 hours 35 minutes

E   7   8 stones = 8 × 14 = 112 pounds   page 90
      William weighs 112 + 3 = 115 pounds = 115 ÷ 2.2 kg = 52.27 kg

D   8   Average speed = $20 ÷ 1$ hour 40 minutes $= 20 ÷ 1\frac{2}{3} = 20 ÷ \frac{5}{3}$ page 90
$$= 20 × \frac{3}{5}$$
$$= 12 \text{ km/h}$$

D   9   Time = 95 ÷ 42 = 2.2619 hours   page 90
      0.2619 hours = 0.2619 × 60 = 16 minutes
      Jane takes 2 hours 16 minutes.

Tick the questions you got right.

Question	1	2	3	4	5ab	5cd	6	7	8	9	10
Grade	G	G	G	G	G	F	E	E	D	D	C

Mark the grade you are working at on your revision planner on page ix.

3-D shapes

- A **net** is a 2-D shape that can be folded into a 3-D shape.

- A **prism** is a shape which has a uniform cross-section.

- A 3-D shape has a **plane of symmetry** if the plane divides the shape into two halves and one half is the mirror image of the other.

Key words

net ☐　plane of symmetry ☐
prism ☐

Example　Draw the net for this 3-D shape.

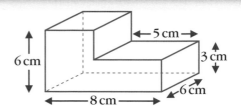

Grade D

① Draw the base.

② Draw the front and back faces.

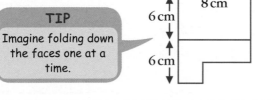

TIP
Imagine folding down the faces one at a time.

③ Draw the remaining faces.

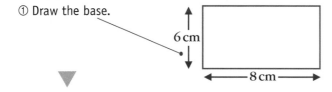

TIP
Remember that edges which will come together must be the same length.

Example　Draw the planes of symmetry for this triangular prism.

Grade D

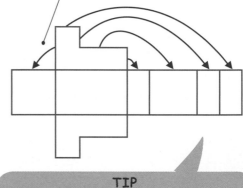

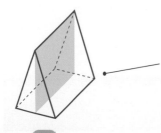

Draw a separate diagram for each plane.

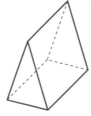

WATCH OUT!
Check that you have found *all* the planes.

- The **plan** of a solid is the view when seen from above.

- The **front elevation** is the view when seen from the front.

- The **side elevation** is the view when seen from the side.

Example

This diagram on isometric paper shows a 3-D shape made from nine cubes.
Draw the plan and elevations for this shape

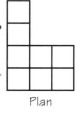

Grade D

① Draw the front elevation.

TIP
Each face of a cube is a square.

Front elevation

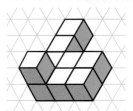

② Draw the side elevation.

Side elevation

③ Draw the plan.

TIP
If you need to draw a 3-D sketch from the plan and elevations, it is best to start by drawing the nearest front face and build the sketch from there.

Plan

Practice

1 Here is a diagram of a 3-D shape.
  (a) Draw the plane of symmetry for the shape.
  (b) Construct the net for the shape.
  (c) Sketch the plan and elevations for the shape.

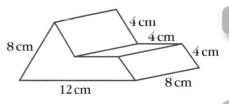

8 cm 4 cm 4 cm 4 cm 12 cm 8 cm

Grade D

2 Draw a sketch of the 3-D prism with this plan and elevations.

Grade D

Check your answers on page 170. For full worked solutions see the CD.
See the Student Book on the CD if you need more help.

Question	1a	1b	1c	2
Grade	D	D	D	D
Student Book pages	256–257	250–253	254–255	249–253

3-D shapes: topic test

Check how well you know this topic by answering these questions.
First cover the answers on the facing page.

Test questions

1   Draw the two planes of symmetry in this solid shape.

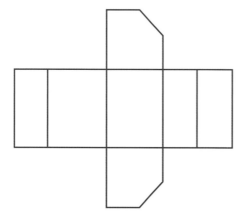

2   Draw a sketch of the solid shape made from this net.

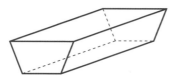

3   Sketch the plan and elevations for this prism.

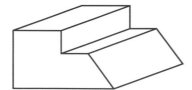

Now check your answers – see the facing page.

Cover this page while you answer the test questions opposite.

Worked answers

Revise this on...

D 1

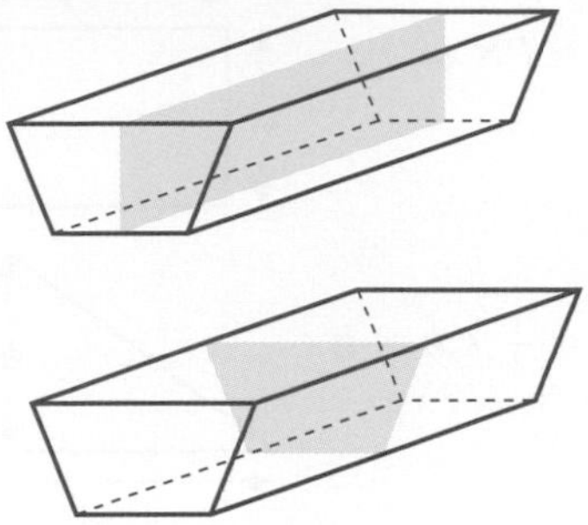

page 90

D 2

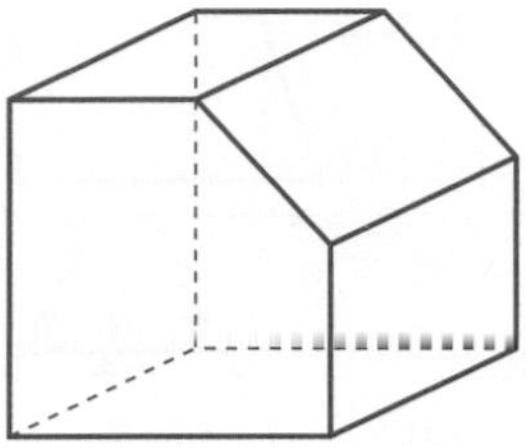

page 90

D 3

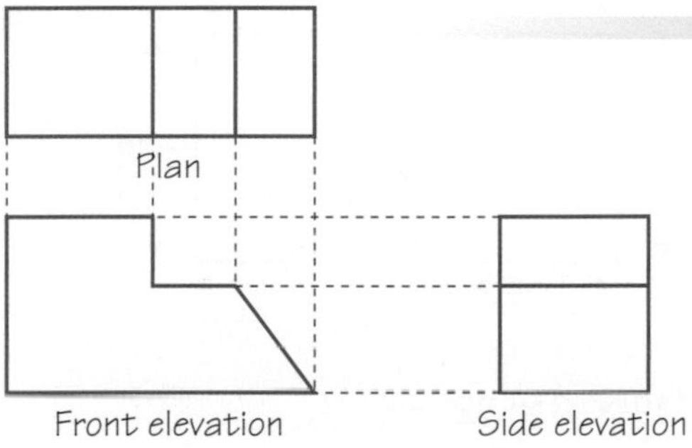

Plan

Front elevation   Side elevation

page 91

Tick the questions you got right.

Question	1	2	3
Grade	D	D	D

Mark the grade you are working at on your revision planner on page ix.

Perimeter and area

- The **perimeter** of a 2-D shape is the distance around the edge of the shape.

- The **area** of a 2-D shape is a measure of the amount of space it covers. Typical units of area are mm^2, cm^2, m^2 and km^2.

- Area of a **rectangle**
  = length × width = $l \times w$

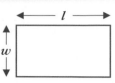

- Area of a **triangle**
  = $\frac{1}{2}$ base × height = $\frac{1}{2} \times b \times h$

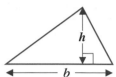

Key words

perimeter	☐
area	☐
rectangle	☐
triangle	☐
parallelogram	☐
trapezium	☐

- Area of a **parallelogram**
  = base × vertical height = $b \times h$

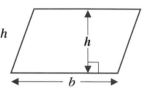

- Area of a **trapezium**
  = $\frac{1}{2}$ × sum of parallel sides × distance between parallels
  = $\frac{1}{2}(a + b) \times h$

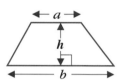

Example

Find the area of this shape.

Grade D

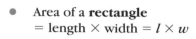

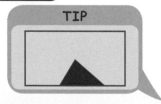
TIP

Decide how to split up the diagram. Here, it is best to complete the rectangle and then subtract the area of the triangle.

Area of rectangle = $12 \times 6 = 72 \, cm^2$

Base of triangle = $12 - 4 - 2 = 6 \, cm$

Area of triangle = $\frac{1}{2} \times 6 \times 3 = 9 \, cm^2$

Area of shape = $72 - 9 = 63 \, cm^2$

- $1 \, m^2 = 100 \times 100 \, cm^2 = 10\,000 \, cm^2$

Example

Change $5 \, m^2$ (5 square metres) into cm^2 (square centimetres).

Grade C

Think of what this area might look like.

$5 \, m^2$ could be a 5 m by 1 m rectangle. This is the same as 500 cm by 100 cm.

$5 \, m^2 = 500 \times 100 = 50\,000 \, cm^2$

TIP
For any question with measurements, it is best to start by deciding which units you want and changing to these.

- The **surface area** is the total area of all the faces of a solid shape.
- A **prism** is a shape which has a uniform cross-section.

Example

Find the total surface area of this prism.

Grade C

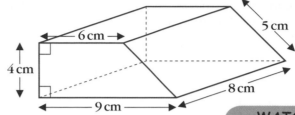

TIP

Imagine 'unwrapping' the four rectangles to make one big rectangle. Its length is the same as the perimeter of the end.

WATCH OUT!

Don't forget the base.

The prism has six faces: two ends and the four rectangles wrapping round these ends.

Area of one end = $\frac{1}{2}(6 + 9) \times 4 = 30\,cm^2$
Perimeter of the trapezium = $4 + 6 + 5 + 9 = 24\,cm$
Total area of surrounding rectangles = $24 \times 8 = 192\,cm^2$
Total surface area = $30 + 30 + 192 = 252\,cm^2$

Practice

1 Find the perimeter and area of this shape. It is made from 1 cm squares.

Grade E

2 Work out the area of this shape.

Grade D

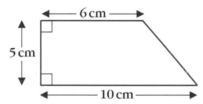

3 Work out the area of this shape.

Grade D

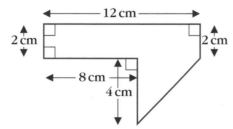

4 Work out the area of this shape in cm².

Grade C

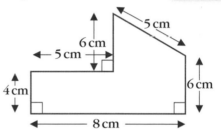

5 Change
(a) 20 000 mm² into cm²
(b) 5 km² into m²

Grade C

6 Work out the surface area of this prism made from six cubes.

Grade C

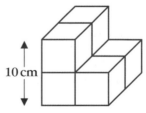

Check your answers on page 170. For full worked solutions see the CD.
See the Student Book on the CD if you need more help.

Question	1	2	3	4	5	6
Grade	E	D	D	C	C	C
Student Book pages	347–351	354–355	354–355	361–363	361–363	357–358

Volume, capacity and density

● **Volume** is the amount of space occupied by a solid object.
Typical units of volume are mm^3, cm^3 and m^3.

● Volume of a **cuboid**
= length × width × height = $l \times w \times h$

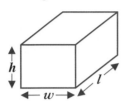

● Volume of a **prism**
= area of cross-section × length

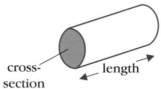

cross-section   length

Key words

volume ☐
cuboid ☐
prism ☐

Example   Change $6\,cm^3$ (cubic centimetres) into mm^3 (cubic millimetres).

Grade C

Think of what this volume ———→ $6\,cm^3$ could be 6 cm by 1 cm by 1 cm.
might look like.   This is the same as 60 mm by 10 mm by 10 mm.

$6\,cm^3 = 60 \times 10 \times 10 = 6000\,mm^3$

● **Capacity** is the amount a container can hold. Typical units of
capacity are millilitres (ml), centilitres (cl) and litres (l).

● In terms of space required, $1\,ml = 1\,cm^3$

● **Density** $= \dfrac{\text{mass}}{\text{volume}}$

Density is measured in g/cm^3 or kg/m^3.

Key words

capacity ☐
density ☐

Example   An open container is in the shape of a cuboid measuring
30 cm by 20 cm by 20 cm.
The container is completely full of orange juice.
The density of the orange juice is $1.1\,g/cm^3$.

Grade C

(a) Work out the volume of the container in cm^3.

(b) Write down the capacity of the container in litres.

(c) How many cups holding 300 ml can be filled from the container?

(d) Work out the mass of orange juice in each cup.

First find the volume. ———→ (a) Volume of cuboid $= 30 \times 20 \times 20 = 12\,000\,cm^3$

Use $1\,cm^3 = 1\,ml$ and ———→ (b) $12\,000\,cm^3 = 12\,000\,ml = 12$ litres
1000 ml = 1 litre

(c) $12\,000 \div 300 = 40$ cups

WATCH OUT!
Check that both
measurements are in
the same units. Here,
both are in ml.

Use mass = density × volume ——→ (d) Volume of orange juice $= 300\,cm^3$
Mass of orange juice $= 300 \times 1.1 = 330\,g$

Practice

Grade E

1 Work out the capacity of a large box in the shape of a cuboid.

The inside of the box measures 100 cm by 60 cm by 45 cm.

Give your answer in litres.

Grade E

2 Work out the volume of this cuboid.

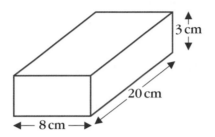

Grade D

3 Work out the volume of this shelf in cm³.

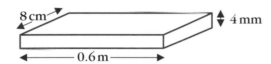

Grade D

4 The volume of this cuboid is 420 cm³. Work out its height.

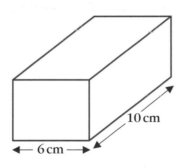

Grade D

5 (a) Work out the volume of this prism.

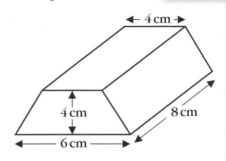

Grade C

(b) The prism is made of glass with density 2.6 g/cm³.
Work out the weight of the prism.

Grade C

6 An ingot of gold has a mass of 4 kg.
The volume of the ingot is 210 cm³.
Calculate the density of the gold

(a) in g/cm³

(b) in kg/m³

Grade C

7 Change

(a) 8 m³ into cm³

(b) 2000 mm³ into cm³

Check your answers on page 170. For full worked solutions see the CD.
See the Student Book on the CD if you need more help.

Question	1	2	3	4	5a	5b	6	7
Grade	E	E	D	D	D	C	C	C
Student Book pages	355–356	355–356	361–363	355–356	488–492	495–496	495–496	361–363

Perimeter, area and volume of shapes

- The perimeter of a circle is called its **circumference**.
  $C = 2\pi r = \pi d$ where r is the radius and d is the diameter.

- Area of a circle $= A = \pi r^2$

- Part of the circumference is called an **arc**.

- A half circle is called a **semicircle**.

- Quarter circles are called **quadrants**.

Key words

circumference	☐
$C = 2\pi r$	☐
$A = \pi r^2$	☐
arc	☐
semicircle	☐
quadrant	☐

Example　The edges of this star are formed by quarter circles with radius 15 cm. Work out the area.

Grade C

The shape is a square with 4 quarter circles removed.

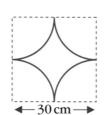

Area of enclosing square $= 30 \times 30 = 900 \text{ cm}^2$

Area removed $= \pi \times 15^2 = 707 \text{ cm}^2$

TIP Work to 3 s.f.

Area of star shape $= 900 - 707 = 193 \text{ cm}^2$

- Volume of a cylinder $= \pi r^2 h$

- Area of the curved surface of a cylinder $= 2\pi rh$

- Total **surface area** of a cylinder $= 2\pi rh + 2\pi r^2$

area of cross-section $= \pi r^2$

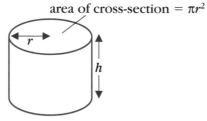

Key words

| surface area | ☐ |

Example　A washer is made from a circular disc of metal, diameter 30 mm, with a circular hole of radius 5 mm.

The washer is 2 mm thick.

The density of the metal is 7.8 g/cm^3.

Work out the mass of 50 of these washers.

Grade C

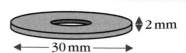

Change all measurements to centimetres. ──────▶ Outer diameter = 3 cm
Inner radius = 0.5 cm
Thickness = 0.2 cm

WATCH OUT!
Remember to work out the outer *radius*.

Find the area of cross-section. ──▶ Area = π × 1.5² − π × 0.5² = 2π cm²

Find the volume. ────────────▶ Volume = 2π × 0.2 = 0.4π cm³

TIP
Leave π in your calculations until the final step.

Use mass = volume × density ──▶ Mass = 50 × 0.4π × 7.8 = 490 g

Practice

Grade D

1 Find the area and circumference of this circular table top.

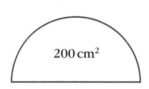

1.2 m

Grade C

2 The area of this semicircle is 200 cm². Work out its perimeter.

200 cm²

Grade C

3 Work out the volume of a cylinder with

   (a) base radius 12 cm and height 8 cm

   (b) base radius 8 cm and height 12 cm.

Grade C

4 A cylinder has a volume of 1280 cm³.
The radius of the base is 15 cm.
Work out the height.

Grade C

5 Work out the total surface area of each cylinder in question **3**.

6 The curved surface area of a cylindrical tin is 150 cm².
The tin is 9 cm tall.
Work out the area of the circular cross-section of the tin.

Grade C

7 A metal washer is a circular disc with a round hole in the middle.
The diameter of the washer is 3 cm and the diameter of the hole is 1 cm. The washer is 2 mm thick.

   (a) Work out the volume of the washer in mm³.

   (b) The washer weighs 10 grams. Work out the density of the metal in g/cm³.

Grade C

Check your answers on page 171. For full worked solutions see the CD.
See the Student Book on the CD if you need more help.

Question	1	2	3	4	5	6	7a	7b
Grade	D	C	C	C	C	C	C	C
Student Book pages	477–482	482–488	489–492	489–492	489–492	489–492	489–492	495–497

Perimeter, area and volume: topic test

Check how well you know this topic by answering these questions.
First cover the answers on the facing page.

Test questions

1 Work out the perimeter and area of this shape.

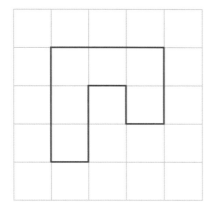

2 The area of this rectangle is 30 cm².
Its length is 10 cm.
Work out its height.

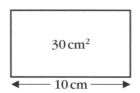

3 Work out the area of this triangle.

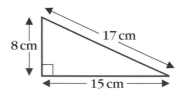

4 Packets measuring 5 cm by 3 cm by 10 cm are packed into a box which measures 50 cm by 60 cm by 30 cm.
Work out how many packets will exactly fill the box.

5 Work out the volume of
   (a) a box which measures 15 cm by 10 cm by 8 cm
   (b) a plank of wood which measures 10 cm by 25 mm by 2 m.

6 The cross-section of a plank of wood is 8 cm by 40 mm. Its volume is 5760 cm³.
Work out the length of the plank in metres.

7 Work out the area of this shape.

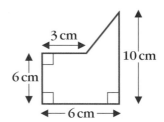

8 The area of a circle is 30.6 cm².
Work out
   (a) the radius
   (b) the circumference.

9 Work out the volume of a cylinder with base diameter 16 cm and height 40 cm.

10 The face *ABCD* of this prism is a trapezium.
AB = 14 cm
AC = 12 cm
CD = 23 cm
Angle *ACD* = 90°
The length is 40 cm.
   (a) Work out the volume of the prism.
   (b) Work out the total surface area.

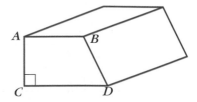

Now check your answers – see the facing page.

Cover this page while you answer the test questions opposite.

Worked answers

Revise this on...

G 1   Perimeter = $3 + 2 + 1 + 1 + 1 + 2 + 1 + 3 = 14\,cm$ page 98
     Area = number of squares = $6\,cm^2$

F 2   Area = height $\times$ 10 = $30\,cm^2$ page 98
     Height = $3\,cm$

E 3   Area = $\frac{1}{2}$ base $\times$ height = $\frac{1}{2} \times 15 \times 8 = 60\,cm^2$ page 98

E 4   The 50 cm side will take a row of ten 5 cm sides. page 100
     The 60 cm side will take a layer of 20 rows using the 3 cm side.
     The 30 cm side (height) will take 3 layers of 10 cm
     Total number of packets = $10 \times 20 \times 3 = 600$

D 5   (a) Volume = $15 \times 10 \times 8 = 1200\,cm^3$ page 100
     (b) Change lengths to centimetres first: 25 mm = 2.5 cm and 2 m = 200 cm
        Volume = $10 \times 2.5 \times 200 = 5000\,cm^3$

D 6   40 mm = 4 cm.   Cross-section = $4 \times 8 = 32\,cm^2$ page 100
                Length = $5760 \div 32 = 180\,cm = 1.8$ metres

C 7   Height of triangle = $10 - 6 = 4\,cm$ page 98
     Base of triangle = $6 - 3 = 3\,cm$
     Area = $6 \times 6 + \frac{1}{2} \times 3 \times 4 = 36 + 6 = 42\,cm^2$

C 8   (a) Area = $\pi r^2 = 30.6$ page 102
           $r^2 = 30.6 \div \pi = 9.74$
            $r = 3.12\,cm$
     (b) Circumference = $2\pi r = 2\pi \times 3.12 = 19.6\,cm$

C 9   Radius = $16 \div 2 = 8\,cm$ page 102
     Volume = $\pi r^2 h = \pi \times 8^2 \times 40 = 8042\,cm^3$

C 10   (a) Area of trapezium (cross-section) = $\frac{1}{2}(14 + 23) \times 12 = 222\,cm^2$ pages 99–100
         Volume = $222 \times 40 = 8880\,cm^3$
     (b) $a^2 = 12^2 + 9^2 = 144 + 81 = 225$
        $a = 15\,cm$
        Perimeter of trapezium = $14 + 12 + 23 + 15 = 64\,cm$
        Surface area = $64 \times 40 + 2 \times 222$
                 $= 2560 + 444 = 3004\,cm^2$

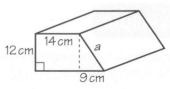

Tick the questions you got right.

Question	1	2	3	4	5	6	7	8	9	10
Grade	G	F	E	E	D	D	C	C	C	C

Mark the grade you are working at on your revision planner on page ix.

Rotation, reflection and symmetry

- A 2-D shape has a **line of symmetry** if the line divides the shape into two halves and one half is the **mirror image** of the other half.

- A 2-D shape has **rotational symmetry** if the appearance of its starting position occurs two or more times during a full turn.

- The **order of rotational symmetry** is the number of times the original appearance occurs during a full turn.

Key words

line of symmetry ☐
mirror image ☐
rotational symmetry ☐
order of rotational symmetry ☐

Example

(a) Draw all the lines of symmetry on this shape.
(b) What is its order of rotational symmetry?

Grade E

Imagine folding the shape in half, ⟶ (a)
as many times as possible.

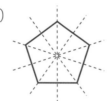

TIP
A regular polygon has the same number of lines of symmetry as sides.

Imagine rotating the shape. ⟶ (b) Rotational symmetry of order 5
How many times does it look the same by the time it comes back to the begining?

- A **reflection** is the image formed by a mirror line called the line of reflection.

- To describe a reflection you need to give the equation of the line of symmetry.

- A **rotation** turns a shape through an angle about a fixed point (the **centre of rotation**).

- To describe a rotation you need to give the centre, the angle, and whether it is clockwise or anticlockwise.

Key words

reflection ☐
rotation ☐
centre of rotation ☐

Example

Describe fully the single transformation which maps shape **P** on to **Q**.

Grade C

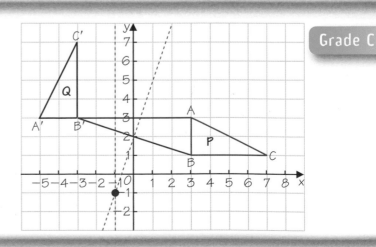

Has the shape been flipped over? (Reflection)
Has it been turned? (Rotation) ⟶ Rotation

▼

Compare corresponding sides on the object and image. ⟶ A'B' is perpendicular to AB. It has turned through 90° anticlockwise.

▼

Find the centre of rotation. ⟶ The centre is at (−1, −1)

Method 1
Test different coordinate points using tracing paper.

Method 2
Draw the perpendicular bisectors of lines joining corresponding points.

Practice

Grade D **1** Rotate the triangle by a half turn about the origin.

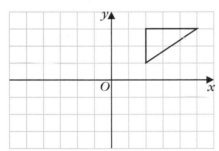

3 (a) Reflect **P** in the y-axis. **Grade C**
Label the image **Q**.

(b) Reflect **Q** in the line y = 2.
Label the image **R**.

(c) Describe fully the single transformation that maps **P** on to **R**.

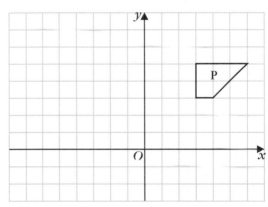

Grade D **2** (a) Reflect triangle **A** in the line x = 5. Label the image **C**.

Grade D (b) Describe fully the transformation that maps **A** on to **B**.

Grade C (c) Describe fully the single transformation that maps **C** on to **B**.

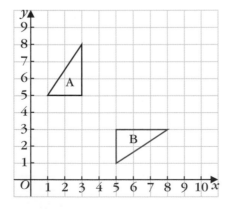

Check your answers on page 171.
For full worked solutions see the CD.
See the Student Book on the CD if you need more help.

Question	1	2ab	2c	3
Grade	D	D	C	C
Student Book pages	414–416		506–512	506–512

Translations and enlargements

- To describe a **translation** (sliding movement) you can give the horizontal (sideways) and vertical (up or down) movements or use a **column vector**.

- An **enlargement** changes the size but not the shape of an object. The **scale factor** of the enlargement is the value that the lengths of the original object are multiplied by.

- In an enlargement, image lines are parallel to their corresponding object lines.

- To describe an enlargement fully you need to give the scale factor and the **centre of enlargement**.

Key words

translation ☐
column vector ☐
enlargement ☐
scale factor ☐
centre of enlargement ☐
similar ☐

Example

Translate shape **A** by the vector $\begin{pmatrix} 2 \\ -3 \end{pmatrix}$.
Label the image **B**.

Grade C

The 'top' number gives the horizontal movement. The 'bottom' number gives the vertical movement.

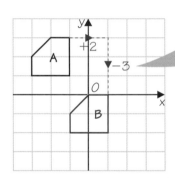

TIP
Vertical movement by -3 means move 3 squares **downwards**.

Example

Enlarge triangle *DEF* by a scale factor of 3 and with centre of enlargement $(-3, 1)$.

Grade C

Mark the centre of enlargement *C*.

▼

Draw a line from *C* through each vertex. The image points will lie along these lines.

▼

Use the scale factor to identify the image points and join them.
Here, $C'D' = 3 \times CD$

TIP
Always check that corresponding sides are parallel.

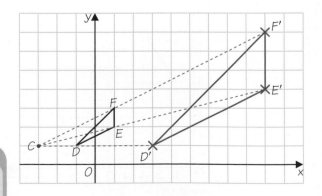

- A scale factor less than 1 means that the image is *smaller* than the object.

Example

Work out the scale factor of the enlargement that maps rectangle *ABCD* on to *FGHI*.

Grade E

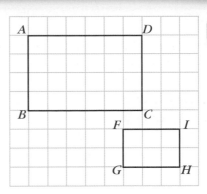

Compare corresponding → Scale factor $= \dfrac{FG}{AB} = \dfrac{2}{4} = \dfrac{1}{2}$
line segments.

Practice

Grade E

1 Enlarge the shape using a scale factor of 3.

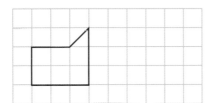

Grade C

2 Enlarge the shape using centre (1, 2) and a scale factor of 2.

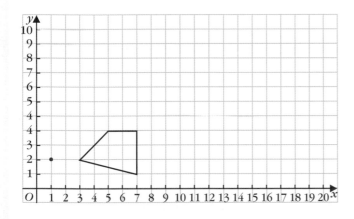

3 (a) Translate the shape **R** by vector $\begin{pmatrix} 1 \\ 2 \end{pmatrix}$.
Label the image **S**.

Grade C

   (b) Translate the shape **S** by vector $\begin{pmatrix} -3 \\ -5 \end{pmatrix}$.
Label the image **T**.

   (c) Describe fully the single transformation that maps **T** on to **R**.

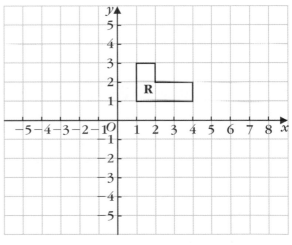

Check your answers on page 171. For full worked solutions see the CD.
See the Student Book on the CD if you need more help.

Question	1	2	3
Grade	E	C	C
Student Book pages	419–421	419–421	504–506

Transformations: topic test

Check how well you know this topic by answering these questions.
First cover the answers on the facing page.

Test questions

1 **(a)** Shade **one** more square so that the shape has one line of symmetry.

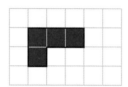

(b) Shade **one** more square so that the shape has rotational symmetry. What is the order of rotational symmetry?

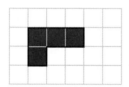

2 **(a)** Translate shape **A** 5 units to the left and 2 units upwards. Label the image **X**.

(b) Translate shape **A** by the column vector $\begin{pmatrix} 2 \\ -3 \end{pmatrix}$. Label the image **Y**.

(c) Rotate shape **A** by a rotation of 90° clockwise with centre of rotation $(1, 3)$. Label the image **Z**.

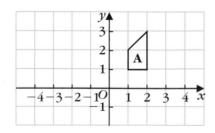

3 Enlarge shape **B** by a scale factor of 1.5 using $(-3, 3)$ as the centre.

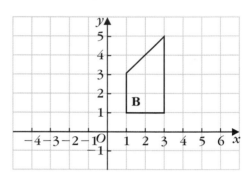

4 Reflect shape **C** in the line $x = y$.

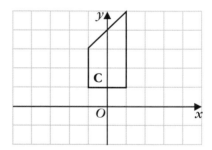

5 Describe fully the transformation which maps **D** on to **E**.

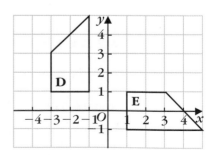

Now check your answers – see the facing page.

Cover this page while you answer the test questions opposite.

Worked answers

Revise this on...

E

1 **(a)** There are several correct answers:

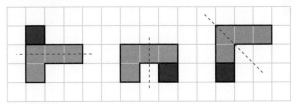

page 106

(b) Order 2

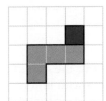

D

2 pages 106 and 108

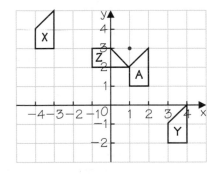

3 page 108

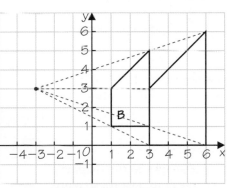

C

4

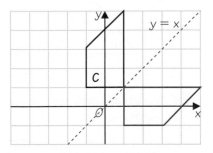

page 106

C

5 A rotation by 90° clockwise with centre $(-1, -1)$

page 106

Tick the questions you got right.

Question	1	2	3	4	5
Grade	E	D	D	C	C

Mark the grade you are working at on your revision planner on page x.

Shape, space and measure: subject test

Exam practice questions

1 Work out the perimeter and area of these shapes.

(a)

5 cm

6 cm

(b)

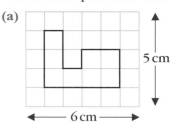

8 cm

13 cm

10 cm

5 cm

20 cm

2 Work out the volume of this prism by counting cubes.

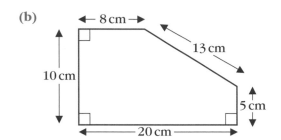

3 Pairs of shapes in the diagram are congruent. List these pairs.

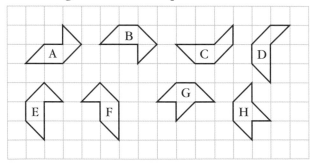

4 Write down the mathematical name for each of these solids.

(a)   **(b)**   **(c)**

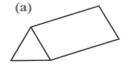 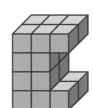

Write down how many faces, edges and vertices each of them has.

5 Copy and draw six shapes to show how the shape tessellates.

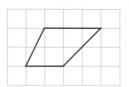

6 Work out the size of the angles marked with letters.
Give reasons for your answers.

(a)

100°

a   34°

(b)

43° 110°

x   y

(c)

30°   c

7 Sketch the plan and elevations for this shape.

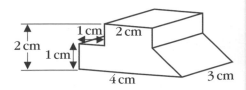

1 cm 2 cm

2 cm   1 cm

4 cm   3 cm

8 The radius of a cylinder is 5 cm and the height is 15 cm.

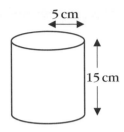

(a) Work out the area of the cross-section.

(b) Work out the volume of the cylinder.

(c) Work out the total surface area of the cylinder.

Give the units with your answers.

9 Work out the surface area of this shape.

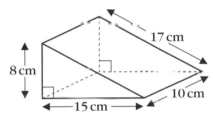

10 The dance floor shown in the diagram measures 10 m by 18 m.

A and *B* are two pillars.

Construct a diagram to show all the points on the dance floor that are more than 2.5 m from walls and pillars.

Use a scale of 1 cm to represent 1 m.

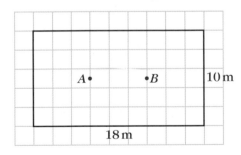

11 Change

(a) 60 000 mm² into cm²

(b) 4 m³ into cm³

12 *A* is 8 km due North of *B*. A ship leaves *A* and travels on a bearing of 120°. Another ship leaves *B* and travels on a bearing of 068°. Using a scale of 1 cm to represent 1 km draw a scale drawing and use it to find how far from *A* the ships' paths cross.

13 (a) Reflect the triangle **T** in the line $y = x$. Label the shape **R**.

(b) Rotate the triangle **T** about $(0, 0)$ through 180°. Label the shape **S**.

(c) Describe fully the transformation that will move shape **S** on to shape **R**.

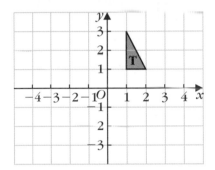

14 Sheila cycles at an average speed of 20 km/h for 2 hours 15 minutes. How far does she cycle?

15 A block of wood is in the shape of a cuboid. It measures 20 cm by 8 cm by 6 cm. The density of the wood is 0.8 g/cm³. Work out the weight of the block.

Check your answers on pages 171–172. For full worked solutions see the CD.

Tick the questions you got right.

Question	1	2	3	4	5	6	7	8	9	10	11	12	13	14	15
Grade	G	G	G	G/F	E	D	D	D	C	C	C	C	C	C	C
Revise this on page	98	100	84	94	84	78, 80	95	102	99	86	99	86	106	90	100

Mark the grade you are working at on your revision planner on page x.

Go to the pages shown to revise for the ones you got wrong.

Shape, space and measure

Angles

- The angles on a straight line add up to 180°.

- The angles at a point add up to 360°.

- The angles in a triangle add up to 180°.

- The angles in a quadrilateral add up to 360°.

- **Alternate angles** are equal.

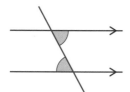

- **Corresponding angles** are equal.

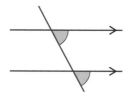

2-D shapes

- The sum of the **exterior angles** of any polygon is 360°.

- The sum of the **interior angles** of a polygon with n sides is $(n \times 180°) - 360°$, or $(n - 2) \times 180°$

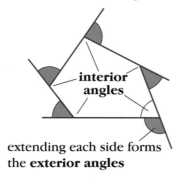

interior angles

extending each side forms the **exterior angles**

- A **bearing** is the angle measured from facing North and turning clockwise.

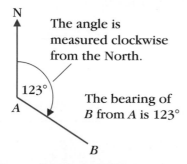

N

The angle is measured clockwise from the North.

123°

A

The bearing of B from A is 123°

B

Measure

- **Average speed** $= \dfrac{\text{total distance}}{\text{total time}}$ (take care with units)

  8 kilometres $=$ 5 miles
  1 kilogram $=$ 2.2 pounds

3-D shapes

- The **plan** of a solid is the view when seen from above.

- The **front elevation** is the view when seen from the front.

- The **side elevation** is the view when seen from the side.

Perimeter, area and volume

- Area of a triangle $= \frac{1}{2}$ base $\times$ height $= \frac{1}{2} \times b \times h$

- Area of a parallelogram $=$ base $\times$ vertical height $= b \times h$

- Area of a trapezium $= \frac{1}{2} \times$ sum of parallel sides $\times$ distance between parallels $= \frac{1}{2}(a + b) \times h$

- The **surface area** is the total area of all the faces of a solid shape.

- **Volume** is the amount of space occupied by a solid object. Typical units of volume are mm^3, cm^3 and m^3.

- Volume of a cuboid $=$ length $\times$ width $\times$ height $= l \times w \times h$

- **Capacity** is the amount a container can hold. Typical units of capacity are millilitres (ml), centilitres (cl) and litres (l).

- In terms of space required, $1\,\text{m}l = 1\,\text{cm}^3$

- Area of a circle $= A = \pi r^2$

Transformations

- You should be able to:
  - perform a rotation with a given centre and angle of rotation.
  - perform a reflection in a given mirror line.
  - describe rotations and reflections fully.

- You should be able to:
  - perform an enlargement with a given centre and scale factor.
  - perform a translation described by a column vector.
  - describe translations and enlargements fully.

Collecting data

- Data which can be counted is called **discrete data**. For example, the number of cars in a car park.

- Data which is measured is called **continuous data**. For example, height in centimetres or weight in kilograms.

- A **tally chart** is a way of recording and displaying data.

Key words

data ☐   continuous ☐
discrete ☐   tally chart ☐

Example

20 people bought cakes at a cake stall. They bought

chocolate	fruit	lemon	banana	fruit
fruit	chocolate	chocolate	fruit	chocolate
banana	chocolate	fruit	chocolate	lemon
chocolate	banana	chocolate	chocolate	fruit

Grade G

(a) Draw a tally chart to show this information.

(b) What special mathematical name is used for this type of data?

Start on the top row and work from left to right on each row. Make a tally mark, |, for each cake bought.

▼

Count up the tallies for each type. Write the numbers in the 'frequency' column.

(a)

Type	Tally	Frequency
Chocolate	ⵉⵀⵉ IIII	9
Fruit	ⵉⵀⵉ I	6
Lemon	II	2
Banana	III	3

TIP

Remember to record 5 like this: ⵉⵀⵉ

WATCH OUT!

Fill in the tallies *and* the frequencies. Students often forget to write in the frequencies.

Data that can be counted is called 'discrete'.

(b) Discrete

- When you are writing questions for a **questionnaire**:
  - be clear what you want to find out, and what **data you need**
  - ask short, simple questions
  - provide **response boxes** with possible answers
  - avoid questions which are vague, too personal, or which may influence the answer (**leading questions**).

Key words

questionnaire ☐   bias ☐
data ☐   leading question ☐
response box ☐

Example

A shopkeeper wants to find out how many chocolate bars students eat. He uses this question in his questionnaire: 'You enjoy eating chocolate bars, don't you?'

Grade D

(a) Explain why this is not a good question to ask.

His next question is 'How many chocolate bars have you eaten?' A few ☐   A lot ☐

Grade D

(b) Write down two things that are wrong with this question.

Grade C

(c) Write down an improved question that the shopkeeper could use. Include response boxes.

Read the question. •───── (a) This is not a good question because it encourages the student to answer 'Yes'.
Is it a leading question? It is a leading question.

EXAMINER'S TIP
You need to explain *why* it is not a good question.

Identify two things wrong •───── (b) You cannot answer 'none' — there need to be response boxes to cover all possible answers. 'A few' and 'a lot' are too vague. The question does not specify a time period.
with the question.
Think about how you could answer it.

TIP
There are three possible answers here. You only need to give two.

EXAMINER'S TIP
Give between 4 and 6 tick boxes.

Design a new question with •───── (c) How many chocolate bars do you eat each week?
a time period and response boxes to cover all possible answers.

0   1   2–4   5–10   more than 10
☐   ☐   ☐   ☐   ☐

Practice

Grade G

1 Peter carried out a survey to find his friends' favourite juices. Here are his results.

orange	grapefruit	cranberry	tropical
orange	tropical	orange	orange
grapefruit	orange	cranberry	tropical
orange	grapefruit	tropical	orange
cranberry	tropical	cranberry	tropical

(a) Draw a tally chart to show Peter's results.

(b) How many of Peter's friends chose grapefruit as their favourite juice?

(c) Which juice was the most popular?

Grade G

2 Which of the following are discrete data and which are continuous?

(a) the height of a door

(b) the number of words on a page

(c) the number of towns in Essex

(d) the weight of a bag of potatoes

3 The owner of a café uses this question in a questionnaire:

'How much money do you spend in the café?'

A lot ☐   Not much ☐

(a) Write down one thing that is wrong with this question.

(b) Design a better question for the café owner to use. Include response boxes.

Grade D

Grade C

4 Holly wants to carry out a survey about pets. She decides to ask some people whether they prefer dogs, cats, hamsters, rabbits or goldfish.
Design a data collection sheet that she can use to carry out the survey.

Grade C

Check your answers on page 172. For full worked solutions see the CD.
See the Student Book on the CD if you need more help.

Question	1	2	3a	3b	4
Grade	G	G	D	C	C
Student Book pages	200–201	231–234	196–198		200–201

Organising data

- A **database** is an organised collection of **information**. It can be stored in a table or on a computer.

Key words

database ☐　　information ☐

Example

This table gives some information about holidays in Spain.

Grade G (a) Write down the name of the hotel at Nerja.

Grade F (b) Which hotels have 15-day holidays for less than £750?

Grade F (c) Which hotels do not have a children's club, and have 8-day holidays for between £500 and £600?

Town	Hotel	Children's club	Price	
			8 days	15 days
Mijas	Neptune	No	555	769
Malaya	Don Paco	Yes	435	649
Nerja	Europa	Yes	495	718
Torremolinos	Cavona	No	602	819
Puerto Banus	Marina	No	595	789

Look down the 'town' column to find Nerja.
Read across that row to find the hotel name.

→ (a) Europa

WATCH OUT!
There may be more than one answer. Students often give only one.

Look down the '15 days' column to find prices less than £750.

→ (b) Don Paco, Europa

TIP
Don't stop when you find one answer. Work through and find *all* the possible answers.

Find the hotels without a children's club. Then look at the 8-day prices for these hotels.

→ (c) Neptune, Marina

- **Distance charts** give the distances between towns.

- **Two-way tables** are used to record or display information that is grouped in two categories.

Key word

two-way table ☐

Example　　**Grade E**

Lucy interviewed 100 people who buy coffee. She asked them which type they buy most, and in which size packets.
Some of her results are given in the table:
Fill in the blanks.

	Instant	Beans	Ground	Total
50 g	3	1	0	
100 g	16			36
250 g	32	9		
Total		18		100

Look for a row or column with one missing value — cell **1**
Fill in this value, which is the total of the three cells above
$3 + 16 + 32 = 51$
Now look for other rows or columns with one missing value, and complete the table, filling in the empty cells in turn

	Instant	Beans	Ground	Total
50 g	3	1	0	³ 4
100 g	16	² 8	⁴ 12	36
250 g	32	9	⁶ 19	⁵ 60
Total	¹ 51	18	⁷ 31	100

TIP
Start with a row or column with only *one* missing value.

TIP
Check that additions work both ways.

Practice

1 This table shows the marks of five students.

Grade G

(a) Which student had the highest English mark?

Grade G

(b) Which students had science marks higher than 25?

Grade F

(c) Which student got 28 marks in two subjects?

Name	English	Maths	Science	History
Stephen	23	29	21	26
Jackie	28	26	29	28
Jason	25	30	23	27
Sakina	26	28	27	32
Mary	32	24	19	25

Grade E

2 Class 11S asked 80 adults which type of television programme they enjoyed most.
The two-way table shows information about some of their answers.

	Comedy	Soap	Documentary	News	Total
Men	7			9	
Women		23	6	2	
Total	19		16		80

Complete the table.

Check your answers on pages 172–173. For full worked solutions see the CD.
See the Student Book on the CD if you need more help.

Question	1ab	1c	2
Grade	G	F	E
Student Book pages	202–206		438–440

Collecting and organising data: topic test

Check how well you know this topic by answering these questions.
First cover the answers on the facing page.

Test questions

1   A teacher asked a class of 20 students how they got to school. They said

| walk | car | bike | bus | train | car | car | walk | train | car |
| train | walk | car | bus | car | car | bus | bus | car | car |

Show this information in a tally chart.

2   This table gives information about cordless electric drills.

Make	Volts	Speed	Torque	Number of gears
Challenger	14.4	700	16	1
Block & Ducker	18	850	5	1
Worker	14.4	1300	24	2
Boss	24	1150	16	1
De Wizz	12	1400	17	2

(a) Which make of drill has a torque value of 24?   (b) Which makes of drill have two gears?

(c) Which makes of drill have speeds between 800 and 1200?

3   Here is a mileage chart:

(a) Use the mileage chart to find the distance between Bristol and Plymouth.

(b) Which two towns are closest together?

(c) Joe travels from Barnstaple to Exeter, then from Exeter to Plymouth, and then from Plymouth to Penzance. How far does he travel altogether?

	Barnstaple					
100	Bristol					
55	84	Exeter				
108	194	110	Penzance			
67	125	44	77	Plymouth		
50	51	34	144	75	Taunton	

4   100 students each study French, Italian or German.
Complete this two-way table, which shows some information about the students.

	French	Italian	German	Total
Boys	21	20		46
Girls	17			
Total			29	100

5   Maddy wants to carry out a survey into how much time people spending listening to the radio.
Here is part of her questionnaire:

> You listen to the radio, don't you? How much?
>
> Sometimes ☐   Always ☐

(a) Write down two things that are wrong with this question.

(b) Write down an improved question that Maddy could use. Include response boxes.

Now check your answers – see the facing page.

Cover this page while you answer the test questions opposite.

Worked answers

Revise this on...

G 1

Travel method	Tally	Total
Walk	III	3
Car	IIIII IIII	9
Bike	I	1
Bus	IIII	4
Train	III	3

page 116

G 2 (a) Worker
(b) Worker, De Wizz
(c) Block & Ducker, Boss

page 119

G 3 (a) 125 miles

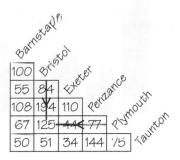

page 118

G (b) Exeter and Taunton

F (c) 55 + 44 + 77 = 176 miles

E 4

	French	Italian	German	Total
Boys	21	20	5	46
Girls	17	13	24	54
Total	38	33	29	100

pages 118–119

D 5 (a) It is a leading question, and the response boxes are too vague.

page 116

C (b) How many hours did you listen to the radio last week?
0–1 ☐   more than 1–2 ☐   more than 2–4 ☐
more than 4–8 ☐   more than 8 ☐

page 116

Tick the questions you got right.

Question	1	2	3ab	3c	4	5a	5b
Grade	G	G	G	F	E	D	C

Mark the grade you are working at on your revision planner on page x.

Charts

- A **pictogram** uses symbols or pictures to represent quantities.

- It needs a **key** to show what one symbol represents.

- A **bar chart** shows data that can be counted. You must leave a gap between the bars.

- A **dual bar chart** compares two sets of data.

Example

Grade F

This bar chart shows the numbers of cars that Evan and Lindsey sold last week.

(a) How many cars did Evan sell on Monday?

(b) On which day did Lindsey sell 9 cars?

(c) Work out the total number of cars sold on Tuesday.

(d) Who sold the greater number of cars on Friday and Saturday?

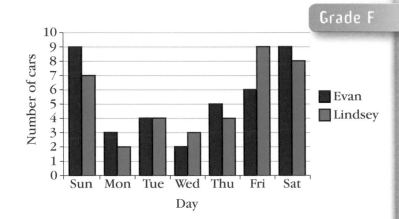

Use the key to see which colour bars show Evan's sales.
Find Evan's bar for Monday and read off the number of sales.

(a) 3 cars

Find 9 on the 'number of cars' axis.
Find a bar for Lindsey that is this height.

(b) Friday

Find the number of cars Evan sold and the number Lindsey sold and add them together.

(c) Evan 4, Lindsey 4
4 + 4 = 8 cars

EXAMINER'S TIP
Show your working

Work out Evan's sales for Friday and Saturday.
Work out Lindsey's sales for Friday and Saturday.
Who sold more?

(d) Evan 6 + 9 = 15
Lindsey 9 + 8 = 17
Lindsey sold more cars.

- A **histogram** shows grouped continuous data.

- A **frequency polygon** shows the general pattern of data represented by a histogram.

Example

Grade C

The table shows the times, in minutes, it takes some people to finish a crossword.

Draw a frequency polygon for this data.

Time, t (minutes)	Frequency
$0 \leq t < 5$	4
$5 \leq t < 10$	8
$10 \leq t < 15$	13
$15 \leq t < 20$	16
$20 \leq t < 25$	6
$25 \leq t < 30$	3

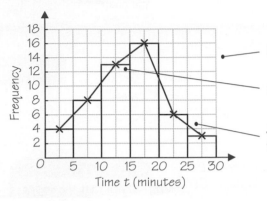

Draw the histogram.

▼

Mark the mid-point of each bar.

▼

Join the mid-points of the bars for the frequency polygon.

EXAMINER'S TIP

You could just plot the mid-points of the bars to draw the frequency polygon.

Practice

1 The pictogram shows the numbers of teas sold in George's café.

(a) Write down the number of teas sold on
   (i) Monday (ii) Wednesday.

(b) 10 teas were sold on Thursday, and 35 teas on Friday. Complete the pictogram.

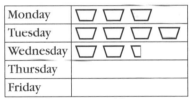

Key: ▱ represents 10 teas

Grade G

2 Here is a dual bar chart to show Stephen's and Lucy's marks in four tests.

(a) What was Lucy's score in English?

(b) In which subject did Stephen score 15?

(c) In which subject did they both score the same?

(d) What was Lucy's total score in all the tests?

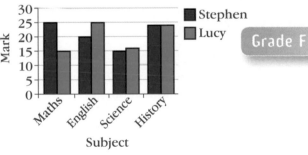

Grade F

3 The table shows some people's weights in kilograms. Draw a frequency polygon for this data.

Grade C

Weight, w (kilograms)	Frequency
$50 \leq w < 55$	2
$55 \leq w < 60$	5
$60 \leq w < 65$	11
$65 \leq w < 70$	13
$70 \leq w < 75$	7
$75 \leq w < 80$	2

Check your answers on page 173. For full worked solutions see the CD.

See the Student Book on the CD if you need more help.

Question	1	2	3
Grade	G	F	C
Student Book pages	229–231	226–229	238–240

123

Pie charts and stem and leaf diagrams

- A **pie chart** is a way of displaying data when you want to show how something is shared or divided.

- The angles at the centre of a pie chart add up to 360°.

Example

Leonie asked 180 Year 9 students 'What is your favourite drink?'

Her results are shown in this pie chart.

Work out the number of students who preferred each drink.

Grade F/E

Measure each angle using a protractor. ──→
Tea: 60° Coffee: 80°
Fizzy: 130° Water: 90°

TIP
Check that the angles add up to 360°.

Work out how many degrees ──→ represent one student.

180 students = 360°
So 1 student $= \frac{360°}{180} = 2°$

Work out the number of ──→ students for each angle.

WATCH OUT!
Remember to *divide* by the angle for each student. Students often multiply.

Tea: the angle is 60°
so the number of students is $\frac{60°}{2°} = 30$

Coffee: number of students is $\frac{80°}{2°} = 40$

Fizzy: number of students is $\frac{130°}{2°} = 65$

Water: number of students is $\frac{90°}{2°} = 45$

Example

Ishmael asked some people their favourite colour.

The table shows his results.

Draw an accurate pie chart to show this information.

Grade E

Colour	Number of people
Red	50
Blue	90
Green	30
Black	70

Work out the total number of ──→ people.

$50 + 90 + 30 + 70 = 240$

TIP
240 people are represented by 360° (the angle at the centre).

Work out the angle for one person.

1 person is represented by $\frac{360°}{240} = 1.5°$

Work out the angle for each ──→ colour.
Multiply the number of people by the angle for one person.

Red: $50 \times 1.5° = 75°$
Blue: $90 \times 1.5° = 135°$
Green: $30 \times 1.5° = 45°$
Black: $70 \times 1.5° = 105°$

EXAMINER'S TIP
Always show your working.

TIP
Check that the angles add up to 360°.

Draw the pie chart carefully, ──→ using a protractor.

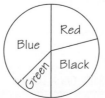

TIP
Remember to label each sector on your pie chart.

- A **stem and leaf diagram** shows the shape of a distribution and keeps all the data values.

- It needs a **key** to show how the stem and leaf are combined.

Key words

stem and leaf diagram ☐

key ☐

Example

Grade D

Jane throws a dart 20 times. Here are her scores:

| 15 | 30 | 23 | 9 | 37 | 42 | 49 | 36 | 49 | 55 |
| 66 | 57 | 69 | 62 | 38 | 31 | 20 | 46 | 17 | 37 |

Draw an ordered stem and leaf diagram to show these scores. Include a key.

Write the data as a stem and leaves.

Use the tens as a stem.

The units are the leaves.

```
0 | 9
1 | 5, 7
2 | 3, 0
3 | 0, 7, 6, 8, 1, 7
4 | 2, 9, 9, 6
5 | 5, 7
6 | 6, 9, 2
```

This question asks for an *ordered* stem and leaf diagram, so now write the leaves in order.

WATCH OUT!

Remember the key! Students often forget, and lose 1 mark.

```
0 | 9
1 | 5, 7
2 | 0, 3
3 | 0, 1, 6, 7, 7, 8
4 | 2, 6, 9, 9
5 | 5, 7
6 | 2, 6, 9
```
Key: 1 | 5 means 15

Practice

Grade F/E **1** Fareed counts the flowers in his garden and draws this accurate pie chart.

Use the pie chart to complete the table.

Flower	Number	Angle
Snowdrop	23	
Crocus	20	80°
Daffodil		
Lily		
Total	90	

Grade F/E **2** Ngaio collected information about the numbers of trees in a wood.
The table shows the results.

Draw an accurate pie chart to show this information.

Tree	Number of trees
Oak	35
Apple	20
Cherry	75
Birch	50

Grade D **3** 20 people were asked

'What are the last two digits of your telephone number?'

Here are the results:

| 08 | 12 | 38 | 24 | 00 | 47 | 07 | 19 | 03 | 02 |
| 31 | 09 | 31 | 22 | 15 | 11 | 03 | 29 | 13 | 06 |

Draw an ordered stem and leaf diagram to represent this data. Include a key.

Check your answers on page 173. For full worked solutions see the CD.
See the Student Book on the CD if you need more help.

Question	1	2	3
Grade	F/E	F/E	D
Student Book pages	384–387	381–387	378–380

Time series and scatter graphs

- A **line graph** can be used to show continuous data.

- A line graph used to illustrate data collected at intervals in time (e.g. hourly, daily, weekly, …) is called a **times series graph**.

Example   The graph shows the percentage of trains that arrived on time each month from January to August.

Grade E

(a) From the graph, write down the percentage of trains that arrived on time in May.

(b) In which month did the highest percentage of trains arrive on time? What was the percentage?

(c) The percentages of trains arriving on time for the rest of the year were

September 90%   October 86%
November 75%   December 89%

Complete the graph for these months.

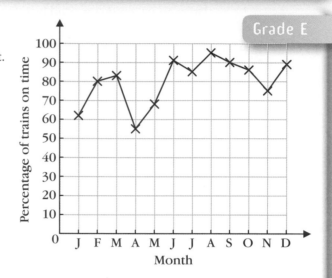

Find the month on the horizontal axis. Read up to the graph and across to the vertical axis.   ——• (a) 68%

TIP
Read all the answers from the graph.

Find the highest point on the graph. Read down for the month and across for the percentage.   ——• (b) August, 95%

WATCH OUT!
Join up the points with straight lines, not with a curve.

Plot each value with a cross ——• (c)
Join the points with straight lines.

- A **scatter graph** shows the relationship between two sets of data.

- A linear relationship between two sets of data is called **correlation**.

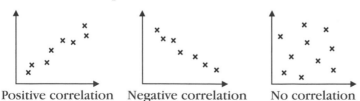

Positive correlation   Negative correlation   No correlation

- The **line of best fit** is a straight line that passes through or is close to the plotted points on a scatter graph.

- A line of best fit can be used to estimate other data values.

The table shows the numbers of pages in nine books and their weights in grams.

Number of pages	65	115	85	125	100	75	145	125	90
Weight (g)	150	260	170	280	220	170	310	260	200

Grade D (a) Draw a scatter graph to represent this data.

Grade D (b) Describe the relationship between the number of pages and the weight.

Grade C (c) Draw a line of best fit on your scatter graph.

(d) Use your line of best fit to estimate **Grade C**

(i) the number of pages in a book of weight 265 g

(ii) the weight of a book with 110 pages.

Plot each pair of values on the scatter graph with a cross. ————— (a)

Identify the type of correlation. ———— (b) As the number of pages increases, the weight increases. It is positive correlation.

Draw a straight line as close to as many of the points as possible. ——— (c) The line of best fit is the solid red line on the graph.

Draw lines across and down, and read off the values. ——— (d) (i) 121 pages
(ii) 242 g

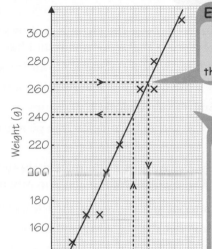

EXAMINER'S TIP
Draw lines on the scatter graph to get accurate readings (to the nearest half-square).

TIP
When drawing a line of best fit it is best to use a clear plastic ruler. There should be roughly equal numbers of points above and below the line.

Practice

1 The table shows the temperatures, in °C, from 08 00 to 12 00 one day.

Grade E

(a) Draw a time series graph for this information.
(b) Estimate a temperature for 11 30.
(c) Describe the general trend in the temperature.

Time	Temperature (°C)
08 00	2
09 00	3
10 00	5
11 00	9
12 00	15

2 The table shows the temperature recorded by a weather balloon at different heights.

Grade D (a) Draw a scatter graph to represent this data.

Grade D (b) What type of correlation do you find?

Grade C (c) Draw a line of best fit.

Grade C (d) Use your scatter graph to estimate
(i) the temperature at a height of 2.4 km
(ii) the height where a temperature of 20 °C might be recorded.

Height (km)	Temperature (°C)
0.4	23
1	17
1.6	12
2	10
2.7	6
3	5

Check your answers on page 173. For full worked solutions see the CD.
See the Student Book on the CD if you need more help.

Question	1	2ab	2cd
Grade	E	D	C
Student Book pages	235–237		447–452

Presenting data: topic test

Check how well you know this topic by answering these questions.
First cover the answers on the facing page.

Test questions

1 Jez has a stamp collection. The pictogram shows the numbers of stamps he has from France, Germany and Italy.

    (a) Write down the number of stamps from France.

    (b) Write down the number of stamps from Germany.

Jez has 60 stamps from Spain and 30 stamps from Austria.

    (c) Use this information to complete the pictogram.

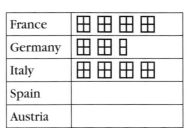

Key: ⊞ represents 20 stamps

2 This accurate pie chart shows information about the medals won by the UK in the Paralympic Games in Athens 2004.

The total number of medals won by the UK was 94.

    (a) Find the number of gold, silver and bronze medals.

    (b) What fraction of the total medals won were silver?

3 An internet company recorded the number of orders it received on each of 30 days.
Here are the results:

    18   48   35   12   43   26   40   14   26   16

    26   13   58   39   36   13   38   57   16   38

    29   44   29   26   44   26   51   52   24   15

Represent this data using an ordered stem and leaf diagram. Include a key.

4 The table shows the test marks for eight students.

Maths	25	6	17	33	21	10	17	28
Science	20	8	15	29	22	9	19	30

    (a) Draw a scatter graph to show this information.

    (b) Describe the relationship between the two sets of data.

    (c) Draw a line of best fit on your scatter graph.

    (d) Fatima's maths mark was 15.
        Use your line of best fit to estimate her science mark.

5 Toby measures the weights of the tomatoes from his tomato plants.
His results are summarised in the table.

    (a) On one sets of axes, draw two frequency polygons to show this information.

    (b) Comment on Toby's plants.

Weight (g)	Frequency plant A	Frequency plant B
30−39	1	3
40−49	2	7
50−59	3	9
60−69	6	7
70−79	5	4
80−89	3	2

Now check your answers – see the facing page.

Cover this page while you answer the test questions opposite.

Worked answers

Revise this on...

G   1   (a) $4 \times 20 = 80$ stamps page 122

  (b) $2 \times 20 + 10 = 50$ stamps   (c)

Spain	⊞ ⊞ ⊞
Austria	⊞ ⦙

Key: ⊞ represents 20 stamps

F/E   2   94 medals are represented by 360°. page 124

  (a) Gold: $\frac{134}{360} \times 94 = 35$ medals   (b) $\frac{30}{94} = \frac{15}{47}$

  Silver: $\frac{115}{360} \times 94 = 30$ medals

  Bronze: $\frac{111}{360} \times 94 = 29$ medals

D   3

1	2, 3, 3, 4, 5, 6, 6, 8
2	4, 6, 6, 6, 6, 6, 9, 9
3	5, 6, 8, 8, 9
4	0, 3, 4, 4, 8
5	1, 2, 7, 8

page 125

Key: 2 | 4 means 24

D   4   (a), (c) pages 126–127

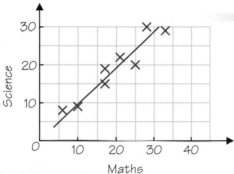

Maths

D   (b) The higher the maths mark, the higher the science mark. It is positive correlation.

C   (c) See graph above.   (d) 15   **Grade C**

C   5   (a) pages 122–123

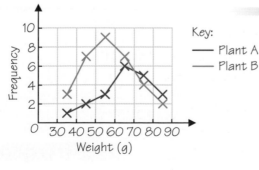

Key:
— Plant A
— Plant B

Weight (g)

  (b) Most tomatoes weigh between
       50 g and 69 g.
       Plant A has heavier tomatoes.
       Plant B has more tomatoes.

Tick the questions you got right.

Question	1	2	3	4ab	4cd	5
Grade	G	F/E	D	D	C	C

Mark the grade you are working at on your revision planner on page x.

Averages and the range (I)

- The **mode** of a set of data is the value which occurs most often.

- The **median** is the middle value when the data are arranged in order of size.

- The **mean** of a set of data is the sum of the values divided by the number of values.

- The **range** of a set of data is the difference between the highest value and the lowest value.

Key words

mode ☐
median ☐
mean ☐
range ☐

Example

Murray made this list of his test marks:

4, 2, 6, 6, 6, 5, 4, 2, 1

Grade G   (a) Write down the mode of his test marks.

Grade G   (b) Work out the median of his test marks.

Grade F   (c) Work out the mean of his test marks.

Grade F   (d) Work out the range of his test marks.

The mode is the number that occurs most often. ———→ (a) Mode = 6

WATCH OUT!
Write the numbers in order before you find the middle one. Students often write down the middle value from the unordered list.

Arrange the numbers in order of size.
Work out the position of the middle number using
$\dfrac{\text{number of values} + 1}{2}$.

———→ (b) 1, 2, 2, 4, **4**, 5, 6, 6, 6

Position of middle number $= \dfrac{9+1}{2} = 5$

The 5th number in the list is '4'
Median = 4

Work out the sum of the values.
Divide by the number of values.

———→ (c) $4 + 2 + 6 + 6 + 6 + 5 + 4 + 2 + 1 = 36$

Mean $= \dfrac{36}{9} = 4$

WATCH OUT!
Find the highest and lowest values. Students often work out the difference between the first and last numbers in the unordered list.

Work out the difference between the highest and lowest values.

———→ (d) Range = 6 − 1 = 5

- With a **frequency table**:

$$\text{mean} = \frac{\Sigma fx}{\Sigma f}$$

the sum of all the $(f \times x)$ values in the table

the sum of the frequencies

Example

Luxni has some boxes of candles.

The table gives information about the numbers of candles in each box.

Number of candles	Frequency
3	4
4	10
5	5
6	1

Grade F (a) How many boxes does Luxni have?

Grade F (b) Write down the modal number of candles in a box.

Grade E (c) Work out the median number of candles in a box.

Grade D (d) Work out the mean number of candles in a box.

Add the numbers in the frequency column. → (a) Number of boxes = 4 + 10 + 5 + 1 = 20

WATCH OUT!
Remember to write down the *value*. Students often write down the frequency.

The mode is the one with the highest frequency. → (b) Mode = 4

The median is the middle value of the data. → (c) Position of middle value = $\frac{20 + 1}{2}$ = 10.5

Boxes 1–4 have 3 candles.
Boxes 5–14 have 4 candles.
So boxes 10 and 11 each have 4 candles.
Median = $\frac{4 + 4}{2}$ = 4

TIP
The number of candles in 10 boxes of 4 is 10 × 4

Add a third column to the table – work out frequency × number for each row. → (d)

Number of candles x	Frequency f	Frequency × number of candles f × x
3	4	12
4	10	40
5	5	25
6	1	6
Total	20	83

Work out the mean. → Mean = total number of candles ÷ total number of boxes
= 83 ÷ 20
= 4.15 candles

TIP
This is the total number of candles.

For more on averages and the range, including practice questions, see pages 132–133.

Averages and the range (II)

- For **grouped data**:
  - the **modal class** is the class interval with the highest frequency
  - you can state the **class interval** that contains the median
  - you can calculate an estimate of the mean using the middle value of each class interval.

Key words

grouped data ☐
class interval ☐
modal class ☐

Example

The table gives information about the weights of 40 small children.

Grade D

(a) Write down the modal class.

Grade C

(b) Write down the class interval in which the median lies.

Weight, w (kg)	Frequency f
$0 < w \leqslant 4$	5
$4 < w \leqslant 8$	13
$8 < w \leqslant 12$	14
$12 < w \leqslant 16$	8

Grade C

(c) Work out an estimate for the mean weight.

Find the class interval with the highest frequency. ⟶ (a) $8 < w \leqslant 12$

Work out the position of the median. ⟶ (b) Position of median
$$= \frac{40 + 1}{2} = 20.5$$

▼

Find the class interval that contains the 20th and 21st values.

Class interval of median is $8 < w \leqslant 12$

TIP

$8 < w \leqslant 12$ has the 19th to 32nd values.

Add two more columns to the table — work out the middle value, x, for each row and $f \times x$ for each row. ⟶ (c)

Weight, w (kg)	Frequency f	Middle value x	$f \times x$
$0 < w \leqslant 4$	5	2	10
$4 < w \leqslant 8$	13	6	78
$8 < w \leqslant 12$	14	10	140
$12 < w \leqslant 16$	8	14	112
Total	40	Total	340

▼

TIP

Add a row for the totals.

Work out the estimate of the mean. ⟶ Estimate of mean
$$= \frac{\text{sum of (middle values} \times \text{frequencies)}}{\text{sum of frequencies}}$$
$$= \frac{340}{40} = 8.5 \text{ kg}$$

WATCH OUT!

Remember to use the *middle* values. Students often use the beginning or end of the class intervals.

Practice

1 Here are the ages, in years, of seven people:

37, 28, 33, 33, 29, 30, 27

(a) Write down the mode. Grade G

(b) Find the median age. Grade G

(c) Work out the range of the ages. Grade F

(d) Work out the mean age. Grade F

2

Number of tries	Number of matches
0	4
1	6
2	11
3	8
4	5

The table gives information about the number of tries scored by a rugby team in each match of the season.

(a) How many matches were there? Grade F

(b) Write down the modal number of tries in a match. Grade F

(c) Work out the median number of tries in a match. Grade E

(d) Work out the mean number of tries in a match. Grade D

(e) Peter said 'The team scored an average of 5 tries per match.' Explain why this is wrong. Grade D

3

Time, t (minutes)	Frequency
$10 \leqslant t < 15$	3
$15 \leqslant t < 20$	9
$20 \leqslant t < 25$	18
$25 \leqslant t < 30$	15
$30 \leqslant t < 35$	5

Bronwen recorded the times, in minutes, it took her to complete 50 crosswords.

(a) Write down the modal class. Grade D

(b) Write down the class interval in which the median lies. Grade C

(c) Calculate an estimate of the mean time it took Bronwen to complete a crossword. Grade C

Check your answers on page 174. For full worked solutions see the CD.
See the Student Book on the CD if you need more help.

Question	1ab	1cd	2ab	2c	2de	3a	3bc
Grade	G	F	F	E	D	D	C
Student Book pages	369–375			454–457			459–461

Averages and the range: topic test

Check how well you know this topic by answering these questions.
First cover the answers on the facing page.

Test questions

1   A radio company records the numbers of complaints about its programmes.

Here are the numbers of complaints about a particular programme on each of nine days:

2, 4, 2, 1, 16, 2, 4, 3, 2

(a) Write down the mode.   (b) Find the median.

(c) Work out the range.   (d) Work out the mean.

2   Mary collects money for a charity.
The table shows the numbers and types of coins that Mary collected last Saturday.

Type of coin	1p	2p	5p	10p	20p	50p	£1	£2
Number of coins	18	35	7	13	9	11	5	1

(a) How many coins did Mary collect?

(b) Write down the modal type of coin that was collected.

(c) Work out the median type of coin.

(d) Calculate the mean value of the coins.

3   In a survey, 50 people were asked how long they spent watching television last weekend.
The results are summarised in the table.

Time, t (hours)	Frequency
$0 \leqslant t < 2$	11
$2 \leqslant t < 4$	15
$4 \leqslant t < 6$	18
$6 \leqslant t < 8$	6

(a) Write down the modal class.

(b) Write down the class interval that contains the median time.

(c) Calculate an estimate of the mean time.

Now check your answers – see the facing page.

Cover this page while you answer the test questions opposite.

Worked answers

Revise this on...

G   **1**   **(a)** Mode = 2   page 130

G   **(b)** Rewrite the numbers in order of size: 1, 2, 2, 2, **2**, 3, 4, 4, 16   page 130
         Median = 2

F   **(c)** Range = highest value − lowest value = 16 − 1 = 15   page 130

F   **(d)** Mean $= \dfrac{1+2+2+2+2+3+4+4+16}{9} = \dfrac{36}{9} = 4$ page 130

F   **2**   **(a)** 18 + 35 + 7 + 13 + 9 + 11 + 5 + 1 = 99 coins   page 131

F   **(b)** Modal coin = 2p

E   **(c)** Position of median $= \dfrac{99+1}{2} = 50$
         Coins 1–18 are 1p coins; coins 19–53 are 2p coins; ...
         So coin 50 is a 2p coin.
         Median = 2p

D   **(d)** Mean $= \dfrac{\text{sum of (values} \times \text{frequencies)}}{\text{sum of frequencies}}$

                   $= \dfrac{\Sigma f \times x}{\Sigma f} = \dfrac{1683}{99} = 17\text{p}$

Coin	Frequency f	f × x
1p	18	18
2p	35	70
5p	7	35
10p	13	130
20p	9	180
50p	11	550
£1 = 100p	5	500
£2 = 200p	1	200
Totals	99	1683

D   **3**   **(a)** Modal class is $4 \leqslant t < 6$ page 132

C   **(b)** Position of median $= \dfrac{50+1}{2} = 25.5$

         The median is the mean of the 25th
         and 26th times.
         The median time lies within the
         $4 \leqslant t < 6$ class interval.

C   **(c)** Mean $= \dfrac{\Sigma f \times x}{\Sigma f} = \dfrac{188}{50} = 3.76$ hours

Time, t (hours)	Frequency f	Middle value, x	f × x
$0 \leqslant t < 2$	11	1	11
$2 \leqslant t < 4$	15	3	45
$4 \leqslant t < 6$	18	5	90
$6 \leqslant t < 8$	6	7	42
Total	50	Total	188

Tick the questions you got right.

Question	1ab	1cd	2ab	2c	2d	3a	3bc
Grade	G	F	F	E	D	D	C

Mark the grade you are working at on your revision planner on page x.

Probability (I)

- Probabilities can be shown on a **probability scale**.

0           $\frac{1}{2}$ 1

impossible   unlikely   even   likely   certain
                   chance

- If all the outcomes are equally likely,

$$\text{probability} = \frac{\text{number of successful outcomes}}{\text{total number of possible outcomes}}$$

Key words

probability ☐	likely ☐
probability scale ☐	unlikely ☐
impossible ☐	even chance ☐
certain ☐	

Example

This fair four-sided spinner is spun.

Draw a 0 to 1 probability scale and mark, with these letters, the probability that the spinner will land on

   (a) 1 (R)   **(b)** a number greater than 1 (S)   **(c)** an even number (T)

Draw a probability scale.
Label each part as you do the question.

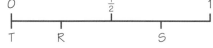

0           $\frac{1}{2}$ 1

T   R   S

Work out the number of successful outcomes.
Divide by the total number of outcomes.
Add the label (**R**) to your probability scale.

(a) $P(1) = \dfrac{\text{number of successful outcomes}}{\text{total number of possible outcomes}}$

$\quad\quad = \frac{1}{4}$

(b) $P(\text{greater than 1}) = \frac{3}{4}$

EXAMINER'S TIP

Do not waste time in the exam by repeating the rule. You have already shown you know it.

There are no successful outcomes, as there are no even numbers.
The event is impossible.

(c) $P(\text{even}) = \frac{0}{4}$

$\quad\quad = 0$

- A **sample space diagram** represents all possible outcomes.

Key words

sample space diagram ☐

Example

Padraig spins a coin and rolls a dice once.

   (a) Make a list of all the possible outcomes he could get.

   (b) Work out the probability that he gets a tail and a 1.

Write out all the possible outcomes. ———• (a) (T, 1), (H, 1), (T, 2),
(H, 2) (T, 3), (H, 3),
(T, 4), (H, 4) (T, 5),
(H, 5), (T, 6), (H, 6)

TIP
Work carefully, following a pattern so that you do not miss any outcomes.

Use the rule
$$\text{probability} = \frac{\text{number of successful outcomes}}{\text{total number of outcomes}}$$
———• (b) $P(T, 1) = \frac{1}{12}$

EXAMINER'S TIP
Use your list from part (a) to answer part (b). Even if (a) is wrong, you can still get full marks for (b).

- If the probability of an event happening is p, the probability of it *not* happening is $1 - p$.

Example

Mrs Coley chooses a drink from a machine. She can choose tea, coffee, chocolate or soup.

The table shows the probabilities that she chooses tea, coffee or soup.

Work out the probability that she chooses chocolate.

Grade D

Drink	Tea	Coffee	Chocolate	Soup
Probability	0.3	0.4		0.1

Add up the probabilities that you know.
———•
$$P(\text{tea}) + P(\text{coffee}) + P(\text{soup})$$
$$= 0.3 + 0.4 + 0.1$$
$$= 0.8$$

TIP
Write this value in the table and check that the probabilities add up to 1.

Subtract from 1. ———• $P(\text{chocolate}) = 1 - 0.8 = 0.2$

- **Two-way tables** can be used to help solve probability problems.

Key words
two-way table ☐

Example

100 students each chose one town to visit last week.
The two-way table shows some information about the students.

(a) Complete the two-way table.

(b) One of these 100 students is picked at random. Write down the probability that the student chose York.

Grade D

	Colchester	York	Chester	Total
Boys			20	52
Girls	13			
Total		41	38	100

Work out the missing values.
For more on two-way tables see pages 118–119.
———• (a)

	Colchester	York	Chester	Total
Boys	8	24	20	52
Girls	13	17	18	48
Total	21	41	38	100

TIP
Check that the rows and columns all add up to the total.

Use the rule
$$\text{probability} = \frac{\text{number of successful outcomes}}{\text{total number of outcomes}}$$
———• (b) $P(\text{York}) = \frac{41}{100}$

TIP
If your number is greater than 1 you have made a mistake.

For more on probability, including practice questions, see pages 138–139.

Probability (II)

- Estimated probability $= \dfrac{\text{number of successful trials}}{\text{total number of trials}}$

- You can use the estimated probability to predict results.

Key words

estimated probability ☐

Example

Grade C

The probability that a biased coin lands 'heads' is 0.7

Henry is going to spin the coin 200 times.

Work out an estimate for the number of times it will land 'heads'.

Rearrange the rule ——————————————• $P(\text{head}) = 0.7$

estimated probability $= \dfrac{\text{number of successful trials}}{\text{total number of trials}}$

Estimated number of heads
in 200 trials $= 0.7 \times 200$
$= 140$

▼

number of successful trials $=$
    estimated probability $\times$ total number of trials

WATCH OUT!

Remember to check that your answer is sensible. Students often put the decimal point in the wrong place.

Example

Grade C

A fair dice is rolled. Work out the probability that it will land on 5 or 6.

Work out the probability of ——————• $P(5) = \frac{1}{6}, P(6) = \frac{1}{6}$
each outcome.

▼

Add the probabilities ——————————• $P(5 \text{ or } 6) = \frac{1}{6} + \frac{1}{6} = \frac{2}{6} = \frac{1}{3}$
together.

WATCH OUT!

Be careful to add the fractions correctly. Students often write $\frac{1}{6} + \frac{1}{6}$ as $\frac{2}{12}$, which is wrong.

TIP

For more on adding fractions see pages 22–23.

Example

Grade C

A bag contains 1 white, 3 black and 5 blue beads.
Omar selects a bead at random.
What is the probability that the bead he chooses is blue or white?

Work out the total number of ——————• Total $= 5 + 3 + 1 = 9$ beads
beads, and the probability of
each outcome.

$P(\text{white}) = \frac{1}{9}, P(\text{blue}) = \frac{5}{9}$

TIP

Write the fraction in its simplest form. For more on simplifying fractions see pages 20–21.

▼

Add the probabilities together. ——————• $P(\text{blue or white}) = \frac{1}{9} + \frac{5}{9} = \frac{6}{9} = \frac{2}{3}$

Practice

Grade F

1. Draw a 0 to 1 probability scale and mark, with these letters, the probability that
   (a) when you spin a coin it will land 'heads' (H)
   (b) it will never rain in England (R)
   (c) when you roll a dice you will get a 6 (S)

Grade D

2. Monty plays a game of draughts with his friend.
   In draughts, games are won, lost or drawn.
   The probability that Monty loses the game is 0.25
   The probability that Monty draws is 0.4
   Work out the probability that Monty wins the game.

Grade E

3. Rhian rolls a blue dice and a red dice.

   (a) List all the possible outcomes.

Grade C

   (b) Use your list to find the probability that she gets a
       total score of 7.

Grade C

4. A fair spinner is made in the shape of a regular hexagon.
   It can land on red, blue or yellow.
   Write down the probability that the spinner will land on red.

Grade D

5. Freddie asked 50 people how they travelled to work.
   The table shows this information.

	Car	Walk	Bus	Train	Total
Men	12			7	24
Women	16		2		26
Total		9	5	8	

   (a) Copy and complete the two-way table.
   (b) Freddie chooses a person at random. What is the probability that he chooses
       (i)   a person that travels to work by train?
       (ii) a man that walks to work?
       (iii) a woman that travels to work by car?

Check your answers on page 174. For full worked solutions see the CD.
See the Student Book on the CD if you need more help.

Question	1	2	3a	3b	4	5
Grade	F	D	E	C	C	D
Student Book pages	425–426	430–432	435–437		426–428	

Probability: topic test

Check how well you know this topic by answering these questions.
First cover the answers on the facing page.

Test questions

1.   This fair six-sided dice is rolled.
   Draw a 0 to 1 probability scale and mark, with these
   letters, the probability that the dice will land on

   (a) a 6   (S)

   (b) an odd number   (T)

   (c) a 7   (V)

2.   Vijay spins this fair spinner and tosses a fair coin.
   Make a list of all the outcomes he could get.
   The first is (1, head).

3.   A box contains beads which are red, yellow, blue or green.
   Helen is going to pick one bead from the box at random.
   The table shows the probabilities that the bead she picks is red, yellow or green.

Colour	Red	Yellow	Blue	Green
Probability	0.15	0.23		0.41

   Work out the probability that she will pick a blue bead.

4.   80 students in Year 10 each study French, German or Spanish.
   The table shows some information about these students.

	French	German	Spanish	Total
Girls	17			46
Boys			20	
Total		23	34	80

   (a) Complete the table.

   (b) One of these 80 students is picked at random.
   Write down the probability that the student studies Spanish.

5.   A fair spinner is made in the shape of a regular octagon.
   It can land on 5 or 10 or 20.
   Write down the probability that the spinner will land on 10.

Now check your answers – see the facing page.

Cover this page while you answer the test questions opposite.

Worked answers

Revise this on...

F **1** (a) $P(6) = \frac{1}{6}$

page 136

(b) $P(odd) = \frac{3}{6} = \frac{1}{2}$

(c) $P(7) = 0$

F **2** (1, head),
(1, tail),
(2, head),
(2, tail),
(3, head),
(3, tail),
(5, head), (5, head)
(5, tail), (5, tail)

page 136

D **3** $P(not\ blue) = P(red) + P(yellow) + P(green)$
$= 0.15 + 0.23 + 0.41$
$= 0.79$

$P(blue)\quad = 1 - P(not\ blue)$
$= 1 - 0.79$
$= 0.21$

page 137

D **4** (a)

	French	German	Spanish	Total
Girls	17	15	14	46
Boys	6	8	20	34
Total	23	23	34	80

page 138

(b) $P(Spanish) = \dfrac{number\ of\ successful\ outcomes}{total\ number\ of\ outcomes}$
$= \frac{34}{80} = \frac{17}{40}$

C **5** $P(10) = \dfrac{number\ of\ successful\ outcomes}{total\ number\ of\ outcomes}$
$= \frac{4}{8} = \frac{1}{2}$

page 136

Tick the questions you got right.

Question	1	2	3	4	5
Grade	F	F	D	D	C

Mark the grade you are working at on your revision planner on page x.

Handling data: subject test

Exam practice questions

1 Salih asked his friends 'What is your favourite sport?'
Here are his results:

soccer	golf	soccer	rugby	cricket
rugby	soccer	soccer	golf	soccer
soccer	rugby	cricket	rugby	soccer
golf	soccer	rugby	soccer	rugby

(a) Complete the table to summarise Salih's results.

(b) Write down the number of friends whose favourite sport was rugby.

(c) What was the most popular sport among his friends?

Sport	Tally	Frequency
Soccer		
Golf		
Rugby		
Cricket		

2 The pictogram shows some information about the numbers of DVDs rented from a petrol station.

(a) Write down the number of DVDs rented on
   (i) Saturday   (ii) Sunday.

(b) 40 DVDs were rented on Monday, and 30 DVDs on Tuesday.
Show this information on the pictogram.

Saturday	⊕ ⊕ ⊕ ⊕
Sunday	⊕ ⊕ ⊖
Monday	
Tuesday	

Key: ⊕ represents 20 DVDs

3 Here is a list of Carol's test marks:

7, 5, 8, 8, 9, 6, 8, 8, 6, 5

(a) Write down the mode.

(b) Work out the mean.

(c) Work out the range.

4 This table gives information about 90 people's eye colour.

Draw an accurate pie chart to show this information.

Eye colour	Number of people
Blue	40
Grey	15
Green	25
Brown	10

5 20 people do a lap round a race track.
Here are their times to the nearest second:

| 62 | 46 | 39 | 53 | 28 | 44 | 65 | 41 | 48 | 37 |
| 36 | 49 | 51 | 46 | 39 | 27 | 60 | 50 | 45 | 33 |

(a) Draw an ordered stem and leaf diagram to show this information. Include a key.

(b) Use your stem and leaf diagram to write down the median.

6 100 students were asked how they came to school that day.
Some of the results are shown in the two-way table.

	Car	Walk	Cycle	Total
Year 7		13	9	41
Year 8	5			22
Year 9		18		
Total	36		21	100

(a) Complete the two-way table.

(b) One of these students is picked at random.
Write down the probability that this student

(i) came to school by car   (ii) is in Year 7 and cycled to school.

7 A freezer contains four flavours of ice-cream – vanilla, chocolate, strawberry and mint.
The table shows the probabilities that Marcus chooses vanilla, chocolate or mint.

Flavour	Vanilla	Chocolate	Strawberry	Mint
Probability	0.2	0.4		0.15

Work out the probability that he picks a strawberry ice-cream.

8 The table shows the heights and weights of ten students.

Weight (kg)	75	65	82	76	71	65	77	70	72	68
Height (cm)	185	182	191	188	184	166	175	178	181	180

(a) Draw a scatter graph to show this information.

(b) What type of correlation do you find?

(c) Draw a line of best fit.

(d) Use your scatter graph to estimate
(i) the weight of a student whose height is 188 cm
(ii) the height of a student whose weight is 74 kg.

Check your answers on page 174. For full worked solutions see the CD.

Tick the questions you got right.

Question	1	2	3a	3bc	4	5	6a	6b	7	8abc	8d
Grade	G	G	G	F	E	D	E	D	D	D	C
Revise this on page	116	122	130		124	125, 130	137		137	126–127	

Mark the grade you are working at on your revision planner on page x.

Go to the pages shown to revise for the ones you got wrong.

Handling data

Collecting and organising data

- A **tally chart** is a way of recording and displaying data.

Flavour	Tally	Frequency
Chocolate	⊥⊢⊢ ||||	9
Fruit	⊥⊢⊢ |	6
Lemon	||	2
Banana	|||	3

- **Two-way tables** are used to record or display information that is grouped in two categories.

Presenting data

- A **pictogram** uses symbols or pictures to represent quantities. It needs a **key** to show what one symbol represents.

Monday	▷☐◁ ▷☐◁
Tuesday	▷☐
Wednesday	▷☐◁ ▷☐
Thursday	▷☐◁ ▷☐◁ ▷☐◁
Friday	▷☐◁

Key: ▷☐◁ represents 10 bags of toffees

- A **bar chart** shows data that can be counted. You must leave a gap between the bars.

- A **dual bar chart** compares two sets of data.

- A **pie chart** is a way of displaying data when you want to show how something is shared or divided.

- The angles at the centre of a pie chart add up to 360°.

- A **stem and leaf diagram** shows the shape of a distribution and keeps all the data values. It needs a **key** to show how the stem and leaf are combined.

```
0 | 9
1 | 2, 3
2 | 0, 7
3 | 4, 8
4 | 1
```
Key: 1 | 2 means 12

- A **line graph** can be used to show continuous data.

Averages and the range

- The **mode** of a set of data is the value which occurs most often.

- The **median** is the middle value when the data are arranged in order of size.

- The **mean** of a set of data is the sum of the values divided by the number of values.

- The **range** of a set of data is the difference between the highest value and the lowest value.

- With a **frequency table**:

$$\text{mean} = \frac{\Sigma fx}{\Sigma f}$$

the sum of all the ($f \times x$) values in the table
the sum of the frequencies

- For **grouped data**:
  - the **modal class** is the class interval with the highest frequency
  - you can state the **class interval** that contains the median
  - you can calculate an estimate of the **mean** using the middle value of each class interval.

Probability

- Probabilities can be shown on a **probability scale**.

```
0                    ½                    1
|--------|-----------|-----------|--------|
impossible  unlikely    even       likely   certain
                       chance
```

- If all the outcomes are equally likely,

$$\text{probability} = \frac{\text{number of successful outcomes}}{\text{total number of possible outcomes}}$$

- $$\text{Estimated probability} = \frac{\text{number of successful trials}}{\text{total number of trials}}$$

Examination practice paper

A formulae sheet is provided at the end of the calculator examination practice paper.

Non-calculator

1 (a) Write the number **eight thousand two hundred and six** in figures. **(1 mark)**

   (b) Write the number 7068 in words. **(1 mark)**

   (c) Write the number 74 875 to the nearest thousand. **(1 mark)**

   (d) Write the value of the 6 in the number 4652 **(1 mark)**

                                                 (Total 4 marks)

2 (a) Draw a line that is 8 cm long in the space below.
     Start from the point labelled *P*.

     P ✕

                                                      (1 mark)

   (b) Mark with a cross (✕), the point on your line that is 3 cm from *P*. **(1 mark)**

                                                 (Total 2 marks)

3 34 people were on a bus.

   18 people got off.
   4 people got on.

   How many people are now on the bus? **(Total 2 marks)**

4 A coin is made from 25% Nickel and 75% Copper.

   (a) (i) Write 25% as a decimal.

       (ii) Write 25% as a fraction.
            Give your answer in its simplest form.

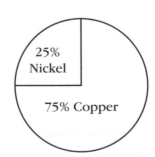

                                               (2 marks)

   The weight of the coin is 12 grams
   25% of the weight is Nickel and 75% of the weight is Copper.

   (b) (i) Work out 25% of 12 grams.

       (ii) Work out 75% of 12 grams. **(2 marks)**

                                                 (Total 4 marks)

5 Here are the first 5 terms of a number pattern.

     2   7   12   17   22

    (a) Write down the next term in this number pattern.   **(1 mark)**

    (b) Work out the 8th term of this number pattern.   **(1 mark)**

    Gabbi says that 235 is a member of this pattern.

    (c) Explain why Gabbi is wrong.   **(1 mark)**

                                                      (Total 3 marks)

6 The pictogram shows the number of packets of toffees sold by a shop some days last week.

Monday	▷☐◁ ▷☐◁
Tuesday	▷☐◁ ▷☐◁ ▷☐◁
Wednesday	▷☐◁
Thursday	▷☐◁ ▷☐◁ ▷☐
Friday	
Saturday	

Key: ▷☐◁ represents 10 packets

    (a) Write down the number of packets of toffees that were sold on

        (i) Tuesday,

        (ii) Thursday.   **(2 marks)**

20 packets were sold on Friday.
15 packets were sold on Saturday.

    (b) Use this information to complete the pictogram.   **(2 marks)**

                                                    (Total 4 marks)

7 Work out

    (i) $3 \times 4 + 2$

    (ii) $12 - 4 \times 2$

    (iii) $24 \div (7 - 3)$ **(Total 3 marks)**

8

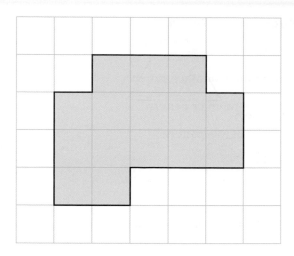

The diagram above shows a shaded shape drawn on a centimetre grid.

(a) Find the area of the shaded shape.
State the units with your answer. **(2 marks)**

(b) Find the perimeter of the shaded shape. **(1 mark)**

The diagram below shows a prism made from centimetre cubes.

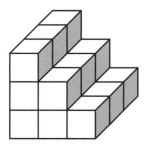

(c) Find the volume of the prism. **(2 marks)**

(Total 5 marks)

9 The table shows the distances in miles between 4 cities.

London			
74	Portsmouth		
39	58	Reading	
97	41	57	Salibury

(a) Write down the distance between Portsmouth and Salisbury. **(1 mark)**

(b) Which two cities are the furthest apart? **(1 mark)**

Russell drives from London to Reading.
He then drives from Reading to Portsmouth.
Finally he drives from Portsmouth to London.

(c) Work out the total distance Russell drives. **(3 marks)**

(Total 5 marks)

10 Here is the net of a 3-D shape.

The diagrams show five 3-D shapes.

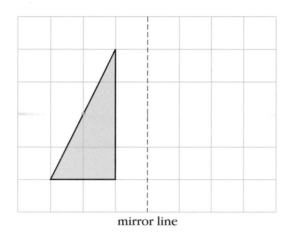

A   B   C   D   E

Write down the letter of the 3-D shape that can be made from the net. **(Total 1 mark)**

11 (a)

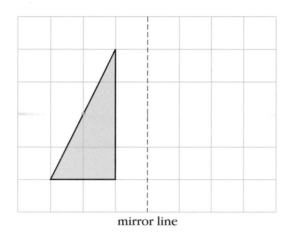

mirror line

Reflect the shaded shape in the mirror line **(1 mark)**

(b)

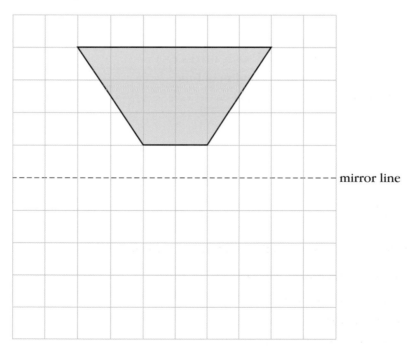

mirror line

Reflect the shaded shape in the mirror line. **(1 mark)**

(Total 2 marks)

149

12

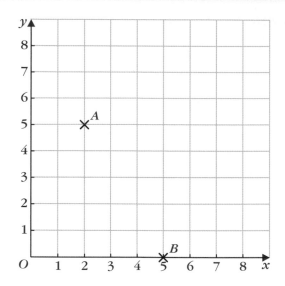

(a) (i) Write down the coordinates of the point A.

(ii) Write down the coordinates of the point B. **(2 marks)**

(b) (i) On the grid, mark the point (7, 3) with the letter P.

(ii) On the grid, mark the point (0, 3) with the letter Q. **(2 marks)**

(Total 4 marks)

13 Simplify

(i) $5g - 2g$

(ii) $p \times p$ **(Total 2 marks)**

14 (a) On the probability scale below, mark with a cross (×)
the probability that it will snow in London in June.

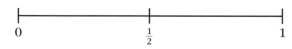

(1 mark)

(b) On the probability scale below, mark with a cross (×)
the probability that it will rain in Manchester next year.

(1 mark)

(c) On the probability scale below, mark with a cross (×)
the probability that you will get a head when you flip a coin.

(1 mark)

(Total 3 marks)

15 **(a)** Draw and mark an acute angle. **(1 mark)**

(b) Draw and mark a reflex angle. **(1 mark)**

(c) Work out the size of the angle marked x.

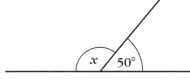

Diagam NOT accurately drawn

(2 marks)

(Total 4 marks)

16 Nathan weighed 20 bags of crisps and recorded the results.
Here are his results, written to the nearest gram.

21	25	29	35	28	32	39	44	33	40
24	26	35	32	39	42	36	27	26	30

(a) Complete the grouped frequency table for Nathan's results.

Weight of crisps	Tally	Frequency
21–25		
26–30		
31–35		
36–40		
41–45		

(3 marks)

(b) Complete this graph to show these results.

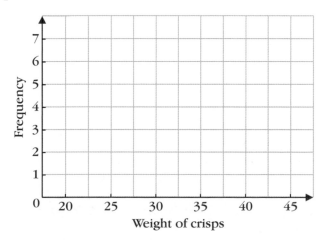

(2 marks)

(Total 5 marks)

17 Jill has a pencil case that contains only 4 pens

1 red pen,
1 green pen,
1 blue pen,
and 1 black pen.

She takes 2 pens at random from her pencil case.

Write a list of all the possible combinations of colours of pens she could choose.
The list has been started for you

(red, green) ....

(Total 2 marks)

18 (a) Work out 325×36 **(3 marks)**

  (b) Work out $2.7 \div 0.45$ **(3 marks)**

(Total 6 marks)

19 Solve the equations

  (a) $2p + 5 = 13$ **(2 marks)**

  (b) $7c + 8 = 4c - 7$ **(2 marks)**

  (c) $5(2f - 6) = 6(f + 1)$ **(2 marks)**

(Total 6 marks)

20 Here are two fractions $\frac{3}{5}$ and $\frac{2}{3}$

Explain which is the larger fraction.
You may use grids like the ones below to help with your explanation.

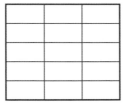 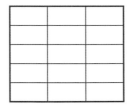

(Total 3 marks)

21 Simon spent $\frac{1}{3}$ of his pocket money on a computer game.

He spent $\frac{1}{4}$ of his pocket money on a ticket for a football match.

Work out the fraction of his pocket money that he had left.   **(Total 3 marks)**

22 Here is a right angled triangle *PQR*.

PQ = 6 cm

QR = 8 am

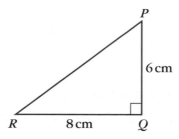

Calculate the length of *PR*. (**Total 3 marks**)

23 The two-way table gives information about the lunch arrangements of 80 students.

	School lunch	Packed lunch	Other	Total
Female	20		14	45
Male		5		
Total	35			80

(**a**) Complete the two-way table. (**3 marks**)

One of the 80 students is chosen at random.

(**b**) What is the probability that the student is female and has a school lunch?
Give your answer in its simplest form. (**2 marks**)

(**Total 5 marks**)

24 On a copy of the diagram use ruler and compasses to construct the perpendicular from *P* to the line *RQ*

P

R ——————————————————————————— Q

(**Total 3 marks**)

25 The diagram shows a large rectangle with two smaller rectangles cut out of it.

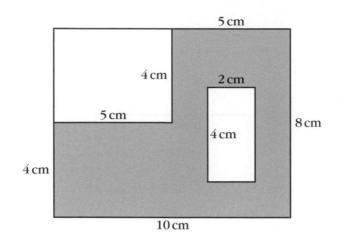

The large rectangle is 10 cm by 8 cm.
The smaller rectangles are 5 cm by 4 cm and 4 cm by 2 cm.

Work out the area of the shaded region in the diagram.

(Total 3 marks)

26 (a) $P = 3g + 7$. Find the value of g when $P = 19$

(2 marks)

(b) Factorise $x^3 - 6x$

(2 marks)

(Total 4 marks)

27 *ABC* is an isosceles triangle
DCB is a straight line
Angle *ACD* = 112°

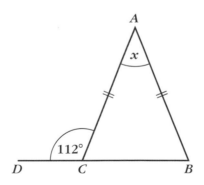

(a) Calculate the value of the angle marked *x*.

(2 marks)

(b) Give reasons for your answer

(1 mark)

(Total 3 marks)

28 A student wants to find out how many take-away meals adults ate.

Design a question that the student could use to find out how many take-away meals adults ate.
You should include some response boxes.

(Total 2 marks)

29 Jake has a biased spinner.
It has five faces coloured Red, Green, Blue, Yellow and Purple.
The probability of getting some of the colours when the spinner is spun is given in the table.

Colour	Red	Green	Blue	Yellow	Purple
Probability	0.4	0.2	0.1		

There is an equal chance of getting Yellow or Purple.

(a) Work out the probabilities of getting Yellow or Purple when the spinner is spun. **(2 marks)**

Jake spins his spinner 50 times.

(b) How many times would you expect the spinner to land on Red **(2 marks)**

(Total 4 marks)

TOTAL FOR PAPER: 100 MARKS

END

Check your answers on pages 175–176. For full worked solutions see the CD.

A formulae sheet is provided at the end of this paper.

Calculator

1 (a) Write one pound forty pence in figures. **(1 mark)**

(b) Write one pound seven pence in figures **(1 mark)**

(Total 2 marks)

2 Each point on the graph represents the size of a shoe and its length, in cm.

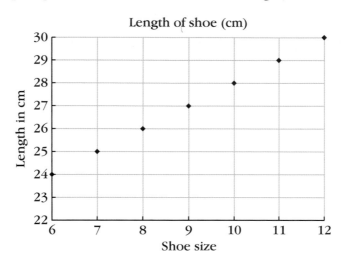

(a) Write down the length of a size 9 shoe. **(1 mark)**

(b) Write down the size of a shoe with a length of 27.5 cm. **(1 mark)**

(Total 2 marks)

3 (a) Write down the number marked by the arrow. **(1 mark)**

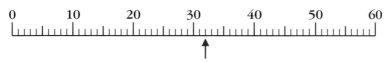

(b) Write down the number marked by the arrow. **(1 mark)**

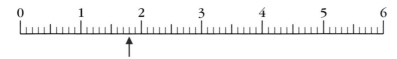

(c) Find the number 240 on the number line.
Mark it with an arrow (↑). **(1 mark)**

(d) Find the number 3.8 on the number line.
Mark it with an arrow (↑) **(1 mark)**

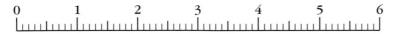

(Total 4 marks)

4 Write down the name of each of these two 3-D shapes.

(i)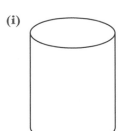

(ii)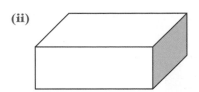

(Total 2 mark)

5 This shape is made from a right-angled triangle, a parallelogram and a quadrilateral.

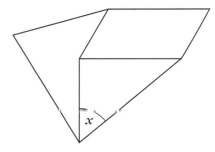

(a) Mark with arrows (≫) a pair of parallel lines.   **(1 mark)**

(b) Mark with the letter *O* an obtuse angle.   **(1 mark)**

(c) Mark with the letter *R* a right angle.   **(1 mark)**

(d) Measure the size of angle *x*.   **(1 mark)**

(Total 4 marks)

6 (a) Measure the length of the line *AB*.

A  B

(1 mark)

(b) Mark the mid point of the line *AB* with a cross
Label this point *P*.

(1 mark)

(c) Draw a circle with centre *P* so that *AB* is the diameter of the circle.   **(1 mark)**

(Total 3 marks)

7 Here is a bar chart showing the number of hours of TV that Helen and Robin watched last week.

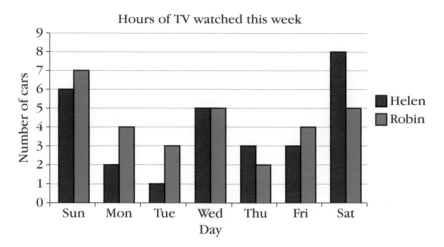

Hours of TV watched this week

(a) Write down the number of hours of TV that Helen watched on Monday. **(1 mark)**

(b) On which day did Helen and Robin watch the same number of hours of TV? **(1 mark)**

(c) (i) Work out the total number of hours of TV that Robin watched on Friday and Saturday.

(ii) Who watched the greater number of hours of TV on Friday and Saturday?
Show your working.

(3 marks)

(Total 5 marks)

8

Pete's Cafe

Price List

Cup of Tea 80p
Cup of Coffee 95p
Can of Cola 75p

Roll £1.60
Sandwich £1.35

Joe buys a can of cola and a roll.

(a) Work out the total cost. **(1 mark)**

Susan buys two cups of tea, and one sandwich.

(b) Work out the total cost. **(2 marks)**

Kim buys a cup of coffee and a roll.
She pays with a £5 note.

(c) How much change should she get? **(2 marks)**

(Total 5 marks)

9 Amanda collected 20 leaves and wrote down their lengths, in cm.
Here are her results.

5   6   5   2   4   5   8   7   5   4
7   6   4   3   5   7   6   4   8   5

(a) Complete the frequency table to show Amanda's results.

Length in cm	Tally	Frequency
2		
3		
4		
5		
6		
7		
8		

(2 marks)

(b) Write down the modal length. **(1 mark)**

(c) Work out the range. **(2 marks)**

(Total 5 marks)

10 The cost of 20 litres of petrol is £18
Work out the cost of 1 litre of petrol.

(Total 3 marks)

11 Complete this bill.

Description	Number	Cost of each item	Total
Spark plug	4	£3.50	£14.00
Wiper blade	2	£2.50	£.........
Light bulb	2	£......	£5.00
Labour charge	$1\frac{1}{2}$ hours at £24.00 an hour		£.........
		Total cost	£.........

(Total 4 marks)

12 (a) Write $\frac{3}{10}$

    (i) as a decimal.

    (ii) as a percentage.   **(2 marks)**

  (b) Shade $\frac{2}{5}$ of a copy of this shape.

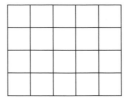

                                             (1 mark)

                                      (Total 3 marks)

13 Here are five shapes.

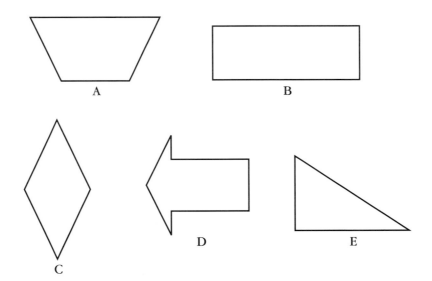

Two of these shapes have only one line of symmetry.

  (a) Write down the letter of each of these two shapes.   **(2 marks)**

Two of these shapes have rotational symmetry of order 2

  (b) Write down the letter of each of these two shapes.   **(2 marks)**

                                      (Total 4 marks)

14 Danny shares a bag of 30 sweets with his friends.

He gives Mary $\frac{1}{5}$ of the sweets.

He gives Ann $\frac{7}{10}$ of the sweets.

He keeps the rest for himself.

How many sweets does Danny keep for himself?   **(Total 3 marks)**

15 Simplify

    (a) (i) $c + c + c + c$

       (ii) $2a + 7a$ **(2 marks)**

    (b) (i) $e + f + e + f + e$

       (ii) $2xy + 3xy - xy$ **(2 marks)**

    (c) $3a + 5b - a + 2b + 8$ **(2 marks)**

    (d) Expand and simplify $x(x^2 + 3x)$ **(2 marks)**

                                        (Total 8 marks)

16 The graph shows the number of ice-creams sold each day during one week.

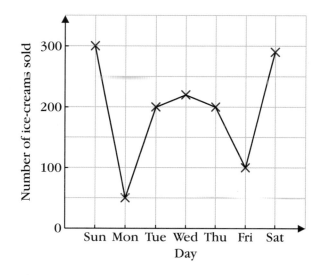

    (a) How many more ice-creams were sold on Sunday than on Monday.   **(1 mark)**

    (b) Explain what might have happened on Monday.   **(1 mark)**

                                        (Total 2 marks)

17 Navjeet uses this rule to work out his pay.

Pay = Number of hours worked × rate of pay per hour

This week Navjeet worked for 12 hours.
His rate of pay per hour was £5.50

    (a) Use this rule to work out his pay.   **(2 marks)**

Last week Navjeet's pay was £78
He worked for 12 hours.

    (b) Work out Navjeet's rate of pay per hour last week.   **(2 marks)**

                                        (Total 4 marks)

18 Here are some patterns made from sticks.

Pattern number 1   Pattern number 2   Pattern number 3

(a) Copy and complete Pattern number 4

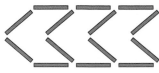

Pattern number 4

(1 mark)

(b) Complete the table.

Pattern number	Number of sticks
1	6
2	10
3	14
4	……………..
5	……………..

(2 marks)

(c) Write, in terms of n, an expression for the number of matchsticks in Pattern number n.   (2 marks)

(Total 5 marks)

19 (a) Work out the area of this rectangle.

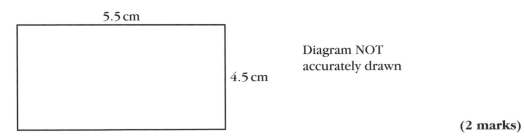

5.5 cm

4.5 cm

Diagram NOT accurately drawn

(2 marks)

(b) A square has an area of 225 cm². Work out the length of one side of the square.

Area 225 cm²

Diagram NOT accurately drawn

(2 marks)

(Total 4 marks)

162

20 Bob lays 150 bricks in 1 hour.
He always works at the same speed.

Work out how long it will take Bob to lay 950 bricks.
Give your answer in hours and minutes.

(Total 3 marks)

21 Joshua rolls an ordinary dice once.
It has faces marked 1, 2, 3, 4, 5 and 6

(a) Write down the probability that he gets

    (i) a 6,   (ii) a number less than 3,

    (iii) an odd number,   (iv) an 8   **(4 marks)**

Ken rolls a different dice 60 times.
This dice also has six faces.

The table gives information about Ken's scores.

Score on dice	Frequency
1	9
2	11
3	20
4	1
5	9
6	10

(b) Explain what you think is different about Ken's dice.   **(1 mark)**

(Total 5 marks)

22 The stem and leaf diagram shows information about the areas of 32 photographs.

```
0 │ 8 8 9
1 │ 1 1 3 4 4 8 9
2 │ 0 3 5 5 7 8 8 9
3 │ 2 2 3 3 5 6 8 8
4 │ 1 1 3 3 5 8
```
Key: 4 | 1 represents 41 cm³

(a) Write down the number of photographs that have an area of 38 cm².   **(1 mark)**

(b) Work out the median.   **(2 marks)**

(Total 3 marks)

23 The top of a table is a circle.
The radius of the top of the table is 40 cm.

Work out the area of the top of the table.

(Total 2 marks)

24 Find the value of $4x + 5y$ when $x = 3$ and $y = -2$ **(Total 2 marks)**

25 The scatter graph shows the Science mark and the Maths mark for 15 students.

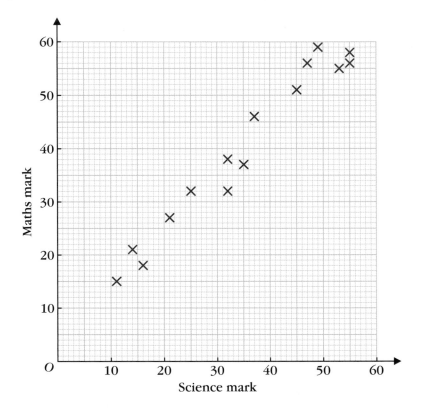

(a) What type of correlation does this scatter graph show?   **(1 mark)**

(b) Draw a line of best fit on the scatter graph.   **(1 mark)**

Sophie's Science mark was 36

(c) Use your line of best fit to estimate Sophie's Maths mark   **(1 mark)**

(Total 3 marks)

26 Ben sails his boat from a port *P* to a lighthouse *L*.

   (a) Measure and write down the bearing of the
       lighthouse *L* from the Port *P.*

       (1 mark)

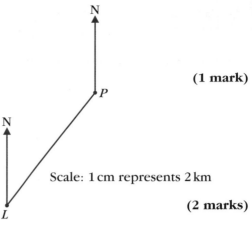

From the lighthouse *L*, Ben sails on a bearing of 300°.
He sails for 12 km on this bearing to a port *Q*.

   (b) Copy the diagram and mark port *Q* with a cross (×)
       and label it *Q*. Use the scale of 1 cm to represent 2 km.

Scale: 1 cm represents 2 km

       (2 marks)

       (Total 3 marks)

27 Amy, Beth and Calvin share 60 sweets in the ratio 2 : 3 : 5
Work out the number of sweets each of them receives.   **(Total 3 marks)**

28 Terri recorded the time, in minutes, taken to complete his last 30 pieces of homework.
This table gives information about the times.

Time (*t* minutes)	Frequency		
$10 \leqslant t < 15$	2		
$15 \leqslant t < 20$	5		
$20 \leqslant t < 25$	10		
$25 \leqslant t < 30$	8		
$30 \leqslant t < 35$	5		

Calculate an estimate of the mean time it took Terri to complete each piece of homework.

       (Total 4 marks)

       TOTAL FOR PAPER: 100 MARKS

       END

Check your answers on pages 175–176. For full worked solutions see the CD.

Formulae

Area of trapezium $= \frac{1}{2}(a + b)\, h$

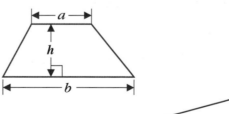

Volume of prism = area of cross section × length

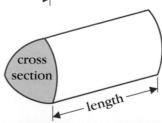

Answers

Place value, ordering and rounding

1 Seventy-five thousand, two hundred and three
2 17 354 000
3 800
4 39, 72, 88, 267, 302
5 (a) 57 000   (b) 56 800

Negative numbers

1 (a) 10   (b) $-10, -6, -2, 0, 2, 6, 10$
2 (a) -1 (b) -11 (c) 1
   (d) -1 (e) 11   (f) 1
3 $2\,^\circ$C
4 (a) -20 (b) -20 (c) 20   (d) -4
   (e) -4 (f) 4   (g) 4   (h) -5

Indices and powers

1 (a) 27   (b) $6, -6$
2 (a) 500   (b) 15
3 $3 \times (4 + 5) = 3^3$
4 (a) 4^5 (b) 9^3 (c) 1   (d) 4^6

Multiples, factors and primes

1 (a) 4, 8 and 16   (b) 4, 8 and 16
   (c) 3 and 5
2 (a) $16 = 2 \times 2 \times 2 \times 2$
   (b) $24 = 2 \times 2 \times 2 \times 3$
3 8
4 48

Calculating and estimating

1 (a) 6970   (b) 28 938   (c) 13 300
2 (a) 25   (b) 24 r8   (c) 31
3 (a) 3   (b) 50
4 (a) 2.973...   (b) 55.233...

Adding, subtracting, multiplying and dividing decimals

1 (a) 15.65   (b) 16.05   (c) £22.85
2 (a) 0.76   (b) 9.15   (c) £2.76
3 (a) 37.8   (b) 66.15   (c) 2.1452
4 (a) 9   (b) 3.2   (c) 12

Rounding decimals

1 Rana £10.50, Axel £8.06
2 £0.90 or 90p
3 (a) (i) 5.5   (ii) 10.4   (iii) 4.1
   (b) (i) 5.45   (ii) 10.40   (iii) 4.06

4 (a) (i) 300 000   (ii) 60 000
     (iii) 0.3   (iv) 0.0006
   (b) (i) 250 000   (ii) 56 900
     (iii) 0.347   (iv) 0.000 600

Understanding and simplifying fractions

1
2 (a) $2\frac{2}{5}$ (b) $\frac{11}{3}$
3 $\frac{3}{4}$
4 For example, $\frac{10}{12}$ and $\frac{15}{18}$
5 $\frac{4}{5}$
6 £15

Working with fractions

1 (a) $1\frac{1}{12}$ (b) $8\frac{5}{24}$
2 (a) $\frac{13}{24}$ (b) $3\frac{5}{12}$
3 (a) $\frac{7}{16}$ (b) 5
4 (a) $1\frac{7}{18}$ (b) $\frac{2}{3}$
5 $1\frac{7}{12}$ miles

Percentages, fractions and decimals

1 $\frac{3}{5}$, 63%, 0.65, $\frac{2}{3}$, 67%
2 (a) 6 kg   (b) £18
3 £32
4 £15
5 She did equally well (75%) in French and Spanish but worse (67%) in German.

Using percentages

1 (a) £76.50   (b) £63.75
2 £188
3 (a) £20   (b) £60
4 20%

Ratio

1 (a) $3:2$ (b) $2:1$ (c) $3:2$ (d) $4:3$
2 $6:4$ and $12:8$
3 (a) (i) $1.25:1$ (ii) $0.667:1$
   (b) (i) $1:0.8$ (ii) $1:1.5$
4 (a) $\frac{5}{8}$ (b) Wayne £15, Tracey £9

Proportion

1 £4.00   2 (a) 5 eggs   (b) 300 g
3 1 km

Number: subject test

1 (a) Seven thousand, four hundred and
thirty-two
  (b) 23 000
  (c) 3 thousands or 3000
  (d) 24 576

2 (a) 8   (b) -10 (c) 6

3 (a) £28   (b) £75.20

4 £56

5 (a) 10 578   (b) 25

6 (a) 72   (b) 12

7 (a) 7500   (b) 1.2876...
  (c) (i) 1.29   (ii) 1

8 (a)   (b) £27

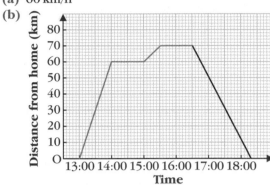

  (c) $\frac{1}{2}, \frac{3}{5}, \frac{2}{3}, \frac{3}{4}$ (d) $\frac{5}{12}$ (e) 8

9 Marco £20, José £12

Simplifying algebra

1 (a) $5e$ (b) $3jk$
2 (a) $8a + b$ (b) $4p^3$
3 (a) $15pq$ (b) t^3
4 (a) h^7 (b) $4x^3$

Expanding brackets and factorising

1 (a) $2c + 12$ (b) $ad - 3d$ (c) $b^2 + 2b$
2 (a) $22p + 2$ (b) $3g + 13h$ (c) $7p + 6$
3 (a) $3(c + 4)$ (b) $4m(m - 3)$ (c) $2t(t - 3)$

Number sequences

1 (a) • • • • •   (b) 16, 19
  • • • • • •
  • • • • •

  Diagram 4

  (c) Multiply 15 by 3, then add 4   (d) $3n + 4$

2 22, 18   3 $7n - 3$

Coordinates

1 (a) (3, 2)   (b) (0, 3)
2 (a) (−2 , −3)   (b) (−3, 1)
3 $(4, 2\frac{1}{2})$
4 $K(3, 3, 0), L(3, 1, 0), M(3, 1, 2), N(0, 1, 2)$

Linear graphs

1 (a) 1 hour   (b) 45 km   (c) 60 km/h
2 (a) 40 m   (b) 10 seconds   (c) 3 m/s
3 (a) 60 km/h
  (b)

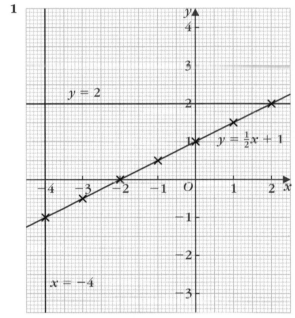

Algebraic line graphs

1

2 (a)

x	-4	-3	-2	-1	0	1	2
y	-1	$-\frac{1}{2}$	0	$\frac{1}{2}$	1	$1\frac{1}{2}$	2

  (b) See graph above.
  (c) (i) $y = 1.25$ (ii) $x = -3.5$

Curved graphs

1 (a)

x	−1	0	1	2	3	4
y	4	0	−2	−2	0	4

(b)

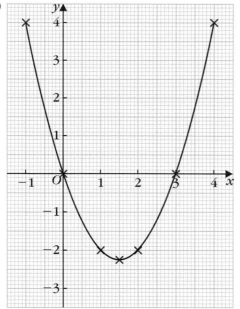

(c) (i) $y = 1.75$ **(ii)** $x = -0.5, 3.5$

2 (a) The sound is immediately loud for a time.
   (b) The sound decreases at a constant rate.
   (c) The sound level remains constant.

Formulae

1 180   **2** £11
3 $W = 8n + kn$ **4** $P = 13y + 3$

Rearranging formulae

1 (a) 4   **(b)** −0.4

2 (a) $x = \dfrac{y + 4}{3}$ **(b)** $x = \dfrac{y - 3}{2}$

3 (a) $x = \dfrac{a - bc}{4}$ **(b)** $x = \dfrac{t - 6}{2}$

4 2.5

Linear equations

1 −9   **2** $6\frac{1}{2}$ **3** −1
4 $4\frac{1}{2}$ **5** $3\frac{1}{2}$ **6** $15\frac{1}{3}$

Solving non-linear equations and inequalities

1 ±7

2 2.4

3

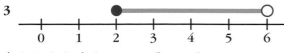

4 0, 1, 2, 3, 4, 5   **5** $x > 3$

Algebra: subject test

1 $2k$ **2** $2g + 12h$ **3** q^3
4 $4y^2$ **5** $3a - 6b$ **6** $6c - 2d$
7 $2x^2 - 3xy$ **8** $3(w - 4)$ **9** $x(x - 5)$

10 (a)

Diagram 4

(b)

x	1	2	3	4	5
y	4	7	10	13	16

(c) $3n + 1$

11 $3n + 5$

12 (a) 120 km   **(b)** 1 hour   **(c)** 80 km/h

13 (a)

x	−2	−1	0	1	2	3
y	−7	−4	−1	2	5	8

(b)

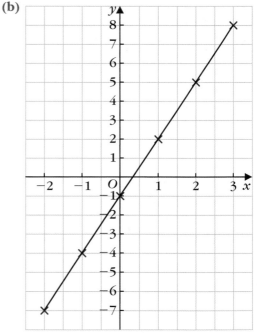

(c) $x = -\frac{1}{2}$

14 £66

15 $T = 3c + 5d$

16 (a) $6x$ **(b)** $6x = 180°$ **(c)** $x = 30°$

17 5

18 9

19 6

20 $3\frac{1}{2}$

21 −3, −2, −1, 0, 1, 2, 3

22 2.8

Naming and calculating angles

1 $x = 113°$ (angles at a point)

2 $w = 25°$ (vertically opposite angles)
$x = 85°$ (angles on a straight line)
$y = 155°$ (angles on a straight line, or angles at a point)

3 (a) 150° Angle $DCB = 30°$
(base angle in an isosceles triangle)
Angle $DCF = 150°$
(angles on a straight line)

(b) 48° Angle $DBC = 30°$
(base angle in an isosceles triangle)
Angle $DBA = 150°$
(angles on a straight line)
Angle $EAB = 48°$
(angles in a quadrilateral)

(c) 90° Angle $DCB = 30°$
(base angle in an isosceles triangle)
Angle $BCG = 60°$
(angle in an equilateral triangle)

Working with angles

1 $a = 47°$ (alternate angles),
$b = 47°$ (corresponding angles),
$c = 84°$ (corresponding angles),
$d = 37°$ (angles in a triangle)

2 (a) 35° (corresponding angles)
(b) 70° Angle $ABE = 110°$
(third angle in an isosceles triangle)
Angle $CBE = 70°$
(angles on a straight line)
(c) 70° (corresponding angles)

3 Angle $ABC = 34°$
(base angle in an isosceles triangle)
Angle $BCD = 34°$ (alternate angles)
Angle $CDB = \frac{1}{2}(180 - 34) = 73°$
(base angle in an isosceles triangle)

4 Triangle PXQ is isosceles.
So angle $PXQ =$ angle PQX
Angle $PYR =$ angle PXQ
(corresponding angles)
Angle $PRY =$ angle PQX
(corresponding angles)
Hence angle $PYR =$ angle PRY and
triangle PRY is isosceles.

Polygons

1 Triangles A and C

2 (a)
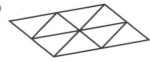

(b)

3 $b = 75°$ (angles on a straight line),
$a = 65°$ (exterior angles sum to 360°)

4 (a) Angle $PTQ = 60°$
(angle in an equilateral triangle)
Angle $QTS = 90°$ (angle in a square)
So angle $PTS = 90 + 60 = 150°$
(b) Angle $PST = \frac{1}{2}(180 - 150) = 15°$
(c) Angle $SPT = 15°$ (base angle in an isosceles triangle)
Angle $XPQ = 60 - 15 = 45°$
Angle $PQX = 60°$
(angle in an equilateral triangle)
Angle $PXQ = 180 - 60 - 45 = 75°$
(angles in a triangle)

5 (a) 105°
(b) $CD = BC = CE$ so triangle BCE is isosceles. Therefore angle $CBE =$ angle CEB

Drawing and calculating

1

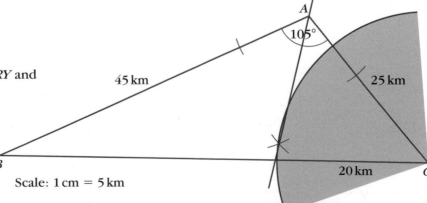

Scale: 1 cm = 5 km

2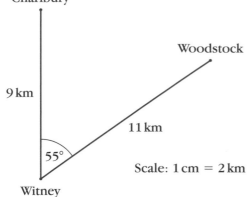

Charlbury

Woodstock

9 km

11 km

55°

Scale: 1 cm = 2 km

Witney

Distance 9.4 km, bearing 106°

(b)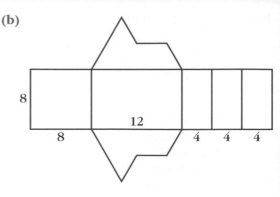

8

8   12

8   4   4   4

(c) Plan   Side elevation   Front elevation

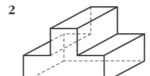

12

4 2 4 2   8   12

8   4 4   4

3

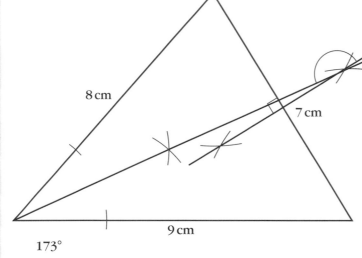

8 cm

7 cm

9 cm

173°

2

4 (a) 53 cm   **(b)** 60 cm
(c) 12.6 cm

Units of measurement

1 (a) 09:15   **(b)** 34 minutes   **(c)** 06:44
2 (a) 7:24 am   **(b)** 275 g
3 (a) 17.6 pounds **(b)** 104 km
   (c) 30 inches
4 12 km/h
5 (a) 126 km   **(b)** 56 km   **(c)** 7 km
6 1000 metres

3-D shapes

1 (a)

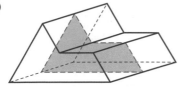

Perimeter and area

1 Perimeter 20 cm, area 18 cm²
2 40 cm²
3 32 cm²
4 44 cm²
5 (a) 200 cm²   **(b)** 5 000 000 m²
6 550 cm²

Volume, capacity and density

1 270 litres
2 480 cm³
3 192 cm³
4 7 cm
5 (a) 160 cm³   **(b)** 416 g
6 (a) 19 g/cm³   **(b)** 19 000 kg/m³
7 (a) 8 000 000 cm³   **(b)** 2 cm³

Perimeter, area and volume of shapes

1 Area 1.13 m², circumference 3.77 m
2 58 cm
3 (a) 3619 cm³   (b) 2413 cm³
4 1.81 cm
5 (a) 1508 cm²   (b) 1005 cm²
6 Radius 2.65 cm, area of cross-section 22.1 cm²
7 (a) 1257 mm³   (b) 7.96 g/cm³

Rotation, reflection and symmetry

1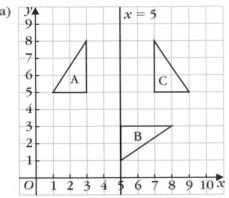

2 (a)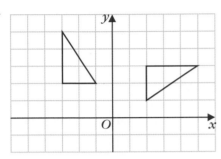

   (b) Reflection in the line $y = x$
   (c) Rotation 90° clockwise about (5, 5)

3 (a) (b)

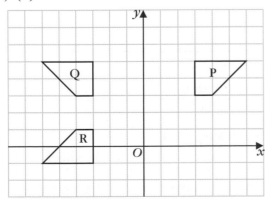

   (c) Rotation through 180°, centre (0, 2)

Translations and enlargements

1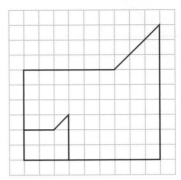

2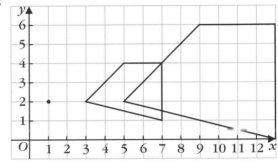

3 (a)
   (b)
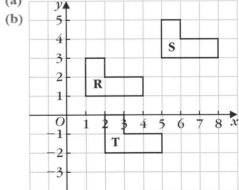

   (c) Translation by $\begin{pmatrix} -1 \\ 3 \end{pmatrix}$

Shape, space and measure: subject test

1 (a) Perimeter 16 cm, area 8 cm²
   (b) Perimeter 56 cm, area 170 cm²
2 20 cubes
3 A and F, B and E, C and D, G and H
4 (a) Triangular prism, 5 faces, 9 edges,
       6 vertices
   (b) Square-based pyramid, 5 faces, 8 edges,
       5 vertices
   (c) Cuboid, 6 faces, 12 edges, 8 vertices

5

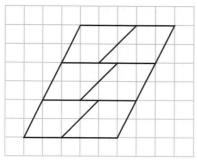

6 (a) $a = 46°$ **(b)** $x = 43°, y = 70°$
  (c) $c = 105°$

7

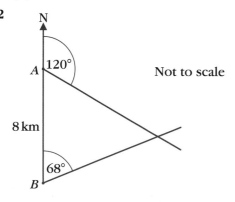

Plan   Front elevation   Side elevation

8 (a) 78.5 cm²   **(b)** 1180 cm³   **(c)** 628 cm²

9 520 cm²

10

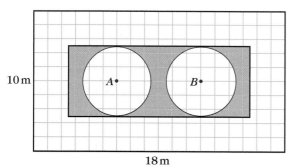

11 (a) 600 cm²
  (b) 4 000 000 cm³

12

Not to scale

9.4 km

13 (a) (b)

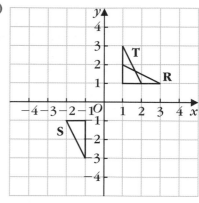

  (c) Reflection in $y = -x$

14 45 km

15 768 g

Collecting data

1 (a)

Drink	Tally	Frequency
Orange	⅂⅂⅂⅂ ‖	7
Grapefruit	‖‖	3
Cranberry	‖‖‖	4
Tropical	⅂⅂⅂⅂ ‖	6

  (b) 3   **(c)** Orange

2 (a) Continuous   **(b)** Discrete
  (c) Discrete   **(d)** Continuous

3 (a) Options are too vague; it is not possible to answer 'none'; no time period specified.
  (b) How much money do you spend in the café in a week?
  £0 ☐   £0.01−£4.99 ☐   £5−£9.99 ☐
  £10−£20 ☐   more than £20 ☐

4

Type of pet	Tally	Frequency
Dog		
Cat		
Hamster		
Rabbit		
Goldfish		

Organising data

1 (a) Mary   **(b)** Jackie, Sakina   **(c)** Jackie

2

	Comedy	Soap	Documentary	News	Total
Men	7	11	10	9	37
Women	12	23	6	2	43
Total	19	34	16	11	80

Charts

1 (a) (i) 30

(ii) 25

(b)

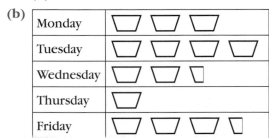

Monday	
Tuesday	
Wednesday	
Thursday	
Friday	

Key: ▱ represents 10 teas

2 (a) 25

(b) Science

(c) History

(d) 80

3

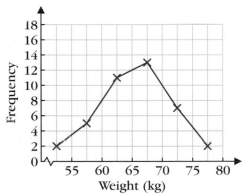

Pie charts and stem and leaf diagrams

1

Flower	Number	Angle
Snowdrop	23	92°
Crocus	20	80°
Daffodil	29	116°
Lily	18	72°
Total	90	360°

2

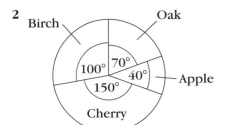

Birch, Oak, Apple, Cherry
100° 70° 40° 150°

3

```
0 | 0, 2, 3, 3, 6, 7, 8, 9
1 | 1, 2, 3, 5, 9
2 | 2, 4, 9
3 | 1, 1, 8
4 | 7            Key: 2 | 4 represents 24
```

Time series and scatter graphs

1 (a)

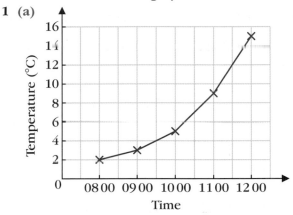

(b) $12-13\,°C$

(c) The temperature is rising steadily.

2 (a) (c)

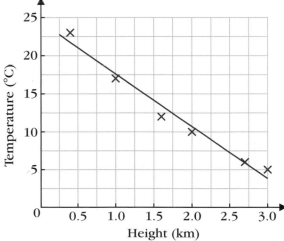

(b) Negative

(d) (i) $8\,°C$ (ii) 0.6 km or 0.7 km

Averages and the range

1 (a) 33   **(b)** 30   **(c)** 10   **(d)** 31

2 (a) 34   **(b)** 2   **(c)** 2   **(d)** 2.12

   (e) The most tries the team scored in any match was 4, so the average cannot be more than 4.

3 (a) $20 \leqslant t < 25$

   (b) $20 \leqslant t < 25$

   (c) 23.5 minutes

Probability

1

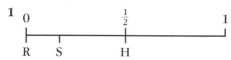

```
0                    ½                    1
|———————————————————|———————————————————|
  R    S             H
```

2 0.35

3 (a) (B1, R1), (B1, R2), (B1, R3), (B1, R4), (B1, R5), (B1, R6)

   (B2, R1), (B2, R2), (B2, R3), (B2, R4), (B2, R5), (B2, R6)

   (B3, R1), (B3, R2), (B3, R3), (B3, R4), (B3, R5), (B3, R6)

   (B4, R1), (B4, R2), (B4, R3), (B4, R4), (B4, R5), (B4, R6)

   (B5, R1), (B5, R2), (B5, R3), (B5, R4), (B5, R5), (B5, R6)

   (B6, R1), (B6, R2), (B6, R3), (B6, R4), (B6, R5), (B6, R6)

   (b) $\frac{6}{36} = \frac{1}{6}$

4 $\frac{3}{6} = \frac{1}{2}$

5 (a)

	Car	Walk	Bus	Train	Total
Men	12	2	3	7	24
Women	16	7	2	1	26
Total	28	9	5	8	50

   (b) (i) $\frac{8}{50}$ **(ii)** $\frac{2}{50}$ **(iii)** $\frac{16}{50}$

Handling data: subject test

1 (a)

Sport	Tally	Frequency
Soccer	ⅠⅠⅠⅠ ⅠⅠⅠⅠ	9
Golf	ⅠⅠⅠ	3
Rugby	ⅠⅠⅠⅠ Ⅰ	6
Cricket	ⅠⅠ	2

   (b) 6   **(c)** Soccer

2 (a) (i) 80   **(ii)** 50

   (b)

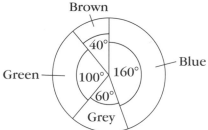

Saturday	⊕ ⊕ ⊕ ⊕
Sunday	⊕ ⊕ ⊖
Monday	⊕ ⊕
Tuesday	⊕ ⊖

   Key: ⊕ represents 20 DVDs

3 (a) 8   **(b)** 7   **(c)** 4

4

Brown, Blue (160°), Grey (60°), Green (100°), 40°

5 (a)

```
2 | 7, 8
3 | 3, 6, 7, 9, 9
4 | 1, 4, 5, 6, 6, 8, 9
5 | 0, 1, 3
6 | 0, 2, 5      Key: 2 | 7 means 27 seconds
```

   (b) 45.5 seconds

6 (a)

	Car	Walk	Cycle	Total
Year 7	19	13	9	41
Year 8	5	12	5	22
Year 9	12	18	7	37
Total	36	43	21	100

   (b) (i) $\frac{9}{25}$ **(ii)** $\frac{9}{100}$

7 0.25

8 (a) (c)

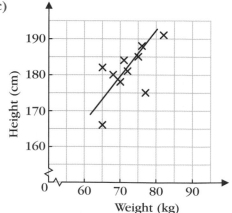

   (b) Positive   **(d) (i)** 77 kg   **(ii)** 184 cm

Examination practice paper: non-calculator

1 (a) 8206
   (b) Seven thousand and sixty-eight
   (c) 75 000   (d) 600

2 (a) Line 8 cm drawn
   (b) Point marked with a cross (×) 3 cm from P

3 20 people

4 (a) (i) 0.25   (ii) $\frac{1}{4}$ (b) (i) 3 g   (ii) 9 g

5 (a) 27   (b) 37
   (c) All members of the sequence end in 2 or 7, 235 does not.

6 (a) (i) 30 packets   (ii) 25 packets

   (b) Friday

   Saturday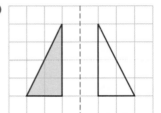

7 (i) 14   (ii) 4   (iii) 6

8 (a) 15 cm^2 (b) 18 cm   (c) 18 cm^3

9 (a) 41 miles   (b) London and Salisbury
   (c) 171 miles

10 C

11 (a)

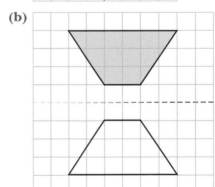

   (b)

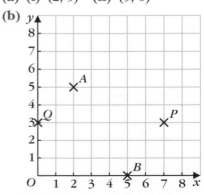

12 (a) (i) (2, 5)   (ii) (5, 0)

   (b)

13 (i) 3g   (ii) p^2

14 (a)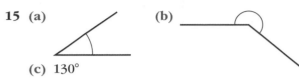

15 (a)   (b)
   (c) 130°

16 (a)

Weight of crisps (g)	Tally	Frequency
21–25	|||	3
26–30	⊬|	6
31–35	⊬	5
36–40	||||	4
41–45	||	2

   (b)

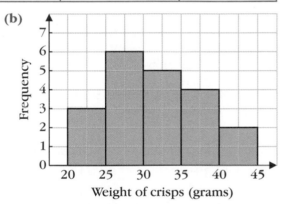

17 (red, green); (red, blue); (red, black); (green, blue); (green, black); (blue, black)

18 (a) 11 700   (b) 6

19 (a) $p = 4$ (b) $c = -5$ (c) $f = 9$

20 Show 9 squares shaded for $\frac{3}{5}$ and 10 squares shaded for $\frac{2}{3}$ then select $\frac{2}{3}$

21 $\frac{5}{12}$

22 10 cm

23 (a)

	School lunch	Packed lunch	Other	Total
Female	20	11	14	45
Male	15	5	15	35
Total	35	16	29	80

   (b) $\frac{1}{4}$

24

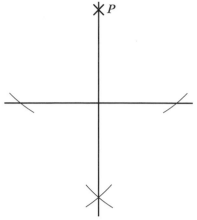

25 52 cm²

26 (a) $g = 4$ (b) $x(x^2 - 6)$

27 (a) 44°

   (b) Angle $ACB = 180° - 112° = 68°$
      (angles on a straight line $= 180°$)
     Angle $CBA = 68°$
      (base angles of an isosceles triangle are equal)
     $x = 44°$
      (angles in a triangle add up to $180°$)

28 For example: How many take-away meals have you eaten in the last month?
   11 or more ☐   5–10 ☐   1–5 ☐   none ☐

29 (a) Yellow: 0.15   Purple: 0.15
   (b) 20 times

Examination practice paper: calculator

1 (a) £1.40   (b) £1.07

2 (a) 27 cm   (b) $9\frac{1}{2}$

3 (a) 32   (b) 1.8

   (c)

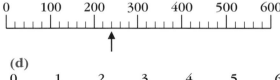

   (d)

4 (i) cylinder   (ii) cuboid

5 (a) (b) (c)

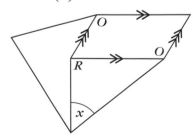

   (d) 51°

6 (a) 4.4 cm
   (b) mid-point marked
   (c) circle drawn (radius = 2.2 cm)

7 (a) 2 hours
   (b) Wednesday
   (c) (i) 9 hours
      (ii) Helen watched the most.
         Helen: $8 + 3 = 11$
         Robin: $4 + 5 = 9$

8 (a) £2.35   (b) £2.95   (c) £2.45

9 (a)

Length in cm	Tally	Frequency
2	I	1
3	I	1
4	IIII	4
5	IIII I	6
6	III	3
7	III	3
8	II	2

   (b) 5 cm   (c) 6 cm

10 90p

11 Wiper blade total £5.00
   Light bulb item cost £2.50
   Labour charge total £36.00
   Total cost £60.00

12 (a) (i) 0.3   (ii) 30%
   (b)

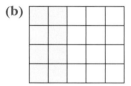

13 (a) A and D   (b) B and C

14 3 sweets

15 (a) (i) $4c$ (ii) $9a$
   (b) (i) $3e + 2f$ (ii) $4xy$
   (c) $2a + 7b + 8$ (d) $x^3 + 3x^2$

16 (a) 250
   (b) The weather might have been cold and wet.

17 (a) £66   (b) £6.50

18 (a)

   (b) Pattern number 4: 18 sticks
      Pattern number 5: 22 sticks
   (c) $4n + 2$

19 (a) 24.75 cm²   (b) 15 cm

20 6 hours 20 minutes

21 (a) (i) $\frac{1}{6}$ (ii) $\frac{1}{3}$ (iii) $\frac{1}{2}$ (iv) 0

    (b) It is weighted (biased)

22 (a) 2   (b) 28 cm²

23 5027 cm²

24 2

25 (a) positive

    (b)

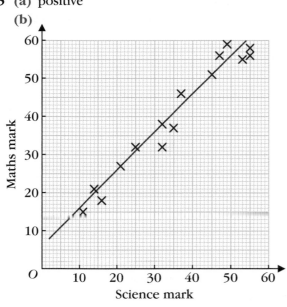

    (c) About 42

26 (a) 216°

    (b)

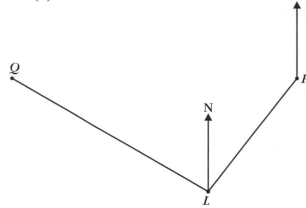

Scale: 1 cm represents 2 km

27 Amy 12 sweets, Beth 18 sweets, Calvin 30 sweets

28 24 minutes

Index